Popular Mechanics

do-it-yourself encyclopedia

The complete, illustrated home reference guide from the world's most authoritative source for today's how-to-do-it information.

Volume 23

STORAGE

to

TABLES

HEARST DIRECT BOOKS

NEW YORK

Acknowledgements

The Popular Mechanics Encyclopedia is published with the consent and cooperation of POPULAR MECHANICS Magazine.

For POPULAR MECHANICS Magazine:

Editor-in-Chief: *Joe Oldham*
Managing Editor: *Bill Hartford*
Special Features Editor: *Sheldon M. Gallager*
Automotive Editor: *Wade A. Hoyt, SAE*
Home and Shop Editor: *Steve Willson*
Electronics Editor: *Stephen A. Booth*
Boating, Outdoors and Travel Editor: *Timothy H. Cole*
Science Editor: *Dennis Eskow*

Popular Mechanics Encyclopedia

Project Director: *Boyd Griffin*
Manufacturing: *Ron Schoenfeld*
Assistant Editors: *Cynthia W. Lockhart*
   Peter McCann, Rosanna Petruccio
Production Coordinator: *Peter McCann*

The staff of Popular Mechanics Encyclopedia is grateful to the following individuals and organizations:
Editor: *C. Edward Cavert*
Editor Emeritus: *Clifford B. Hicks*
Production: *Layla Productions*
Production Director: *Lori Stein*
Book Design: *The Bentwood Studio*
Art Director: *Jos. Trautwein*
Design Consultant: *Suzanne Bennett & Associates*
Illustrations: *AP Graphics, Evelyne Johnson Associates, Popular Mechanics Magazine, Vantage Art.*

Contributing Writers: James R. Berry, *Hutch table of solid pine,* page 2939; Stephen A. Booth, *VCR's expanding universe,* page 2902; Carl Caiati, *Home video special effects,* page 2913; Rosario Capotosto, *Building a stack of swinger,* page 2830, *Stacking tray tables,* page 2930; Sven Corsak, *Picturesque Poolhouse,* page 2862, Frank H. Day, *Snack table,* page 2924, George L. Hall, *TV and Video,* page 2878, Jackson Hand, *Contemporary pedestal table,* page 2916, Len Hilt, *Go fly a kite,* page 2836, Jorma Hyypia, *TV interference problems,* page 2898, David Lander, *third generation,* page 2885, Wayne C. Lecky, *Nesting party tables,* page 2926, James M. Miller, *Swimming pool filter you can make,* page 2858, Elmer K. Norton, *Restring your own tennis racket,* page 2843, Walter Salm, VCR *tuneup,* page 2907, William Schremp, *Parsons table* page 2919, Mort Schultz, *Shock absorbers,* page 2850, Don Shiner, *Cabana for your pool,* page 2859, Marc Stern, *TV antenna selection,* page 2892, Frank Vizar, *VCR saves your slides and movies,* page 2911, *Home video special effects,* page 2913, Harry Wicks, *Diving decks gives added storage,* page 2866, *Back-yard resort from your above-ground pool,* page 2870, *Early American hutch table,* page 2934.

Picture Credits: Popular Mechanics Encyclopedia is grateful to the following for permission to reprint their photographs: R.C.A. Corp., page 2884 (right); George Retseck, pages 2882 (left and right), and 2883; Sheridan Carpet Mills—A Lancer Co., page 2857 for more information call 800-241-4063; Sony Corp. of America, page 2878 (bottom).

ISBN 0-87851-176-8
Library of Congress 85-81760

10 9 8 7 6 5 4 3 2
PRINTED IN THE UNITED STATES OF AMERICA

Although every effort has been made to ensure the accuracy and completeness of the information in this book, Hearst Direct Books makes no guarantees, stated or implied, nor will they be liable in the event of misinterpretation or human error made by the reader, or for any typographical errors that may appear. WORK SAFELY WITH HAND TOOLS. WEAR SAFETY GOGGLES. READ MANUFACTURER'S INSTRUCTIONS AND WARNINGS FOR ALL PRODUCTS.

Contents

VOLUME 23 • ST to TH

STORAGE
Storage space can be found 2820
New look for a tired wall 2828
Build a stack of swingers 2830
See also Bookcases .... Vol. 4
See also Cabinets .... Vol. 4
See also Chests .... Vol. 5
See also Closets .... Vol. 6
See also Garages .... Vol. 11
See also Home Improvement Projects .. Vol. 13
See also Room Dividers .... Vol. 20
See also Sewing Cabinets .... Vol. 21

STUDY CENTERS
See Desks .... Vol. 7

SUMMER SPORTS
Putting green from artificial turf 2833
Go fly a kite 2836
Restring your own tennis racket 2843
See also Camping .... Vol. 5
See also Hobbies .... Vol. 13
See also Weekend Safety Tips .... Vol. 25

SUSPENSION & STEERING SYSTEMS, AUTO
Steering and suspension systems
   service 2846
Shock absorbers 2850
See also Auto Care .... Vol. 2
See also Tires .... Vol. 24
See also Transmissions and Drive Line .. Vol. 25

SWIMMING SAFETY
See Weekend Safety Tips .... Vol. 25

SWIMMING POOL MAINTENANCE
Swimming pool shape-up 2854
Swimming pool filter you can make 2858

SWIMMING POOL IMPROVEMENTS
Cabana for your pool 2859
Picturesque poolhouse 2862
Diving deck gives added storage 2866
Back-yard resort from your
   above-ground pool 2870
Vacation all summer in a low-cost pool ... 2875
See also Decks .... Vol. 7
See also Patios .... Vol. 17
See also Yard and Garden Shelters ..... Vol. 27

SWINGS
See Playgrounds .... Vol. 18

TV AND VIDEO
TV and video 2878
TV's third generation 2885

TV antenna selection 2888
TV antenna installation 2893
TV hits the road 2896
TV interference problems 2898
VCRs expanding universe 2902
VCR tuneup 2907
Videotape selection 2909
VCR saves your slides and movies 2911
Home video special effects 2913
See also Cassette Recorders .... Vol. 5
See also Computer Monitors .... Vol. 6
See also Electronics .... Vol. 8

TABLE SAWS
See Bench Saws .... Vol. 3

TABLES
Contemporary pedestal table 2916
Parsons table 2919
French provincial table 2920
Snack table 2924
Nesting party tables 2926
Stacking tray tables 2930
Early American hutch table 2934
Hutch table of solid pine 2939
See also Bedroom Furniture .... Vol. 3
See also Children's Furniture .... Vol. 5
See also Desks .... Vol. 7
See also Dining Room Furniture .... Vol. 7
See also Furniture Projects .... Vol. 11
See also Outdoor Furniture .... Vol. 16
See also Pool Tables .... Vol. 19
See also Servers .... Vol. 21

TAPE RECORDERS
See Cassette Recorders .... Vol. 5

TARGET SHOOTING
See Marksmanship .... Vol. 15

TELEPHONES
See Weekend Projects .... Vol. 26

TELESCOPES
See Binoculars & Telescopes .... Vol. 3

TERMITES
See Insects .... Vol. 14

THERMOMETERS
See Weather Instruments .... Vol. 25

THERMOSTATS
See Heating Systems .... Vol. 12

INDEX 2943

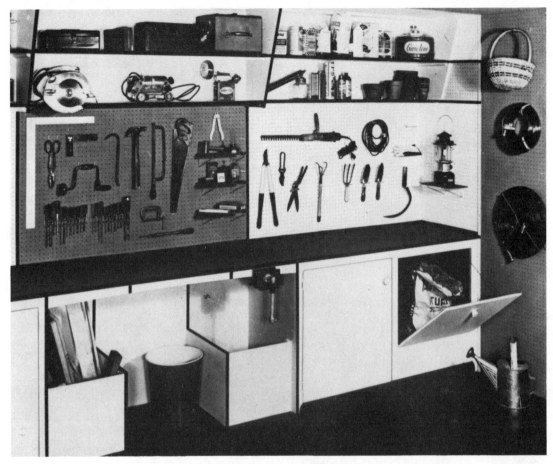

GARAGE-WALL storage unit is a double-duty built-in that provides both work and storage space. It doesn't take as much space as it looks, and can be made to take only two feet off the end of a garage. The long workbench is especially handy for car and yard-tool fix-it jobs that require a long layout area. There's a great deal of storage space both above and below.

Storage space can be found

■ LOOKING FOR MORE STORAGE space? Today, the answer isn't just another trunk in the attic. In the modern equipment-packed home, you need to hide things away and still have them at your fingertips, ready for instant use. There's the movie projector, the stereo, your prized fishing, hunting and photographic gear, countless tools and toys, games and hobby supplies, skis and tennis rackets and baseball bats, kitchen and laundry appliances, a model train or road-race set—all must have their place yet be kept handy if you're going to use and enjoy them. On these pages you will find a number of ideas for versatile, space-saving storage arrangements that can make living more efficient and fun.

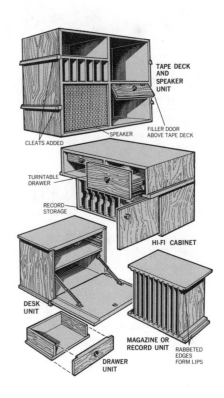

TAPE DECK AND SPEAKER UNIT

FILLER DOOR ABOVE TAPE DECK

SPEAKER

CLEATS ADDED

TURNTABLE DRAWER

RECORD STORAGE

HI-FI CABINET

DESK UNIT

MAGAZINE OR RECORD UNIT

RABBETED EDGES FORM LIPS

DRAWER UNIT

Interchangeable storage units slide in and out on tracks in two clever walls above. At left, strips of grooved plywood provide ready-made slots. Right, bevel siding nailed upside down forms support ledges. Drawings show units that can be built to slide into place.

High off the floor, wall-hung cupboards don't block car, leave parking space underneath for bikes and other bulky gear. Each 3-foot-wide section is a different color for handsome appearance. Doors of perforated hardboard cost little and help to provide needed ventilation to prevent any mildew from forming inside. The front half of an old stepladder rested against the cabinets is especially handy for reaching the upper shelves. If even more storage is desired, full-length cabinets (right) can be added to line the side walls of the garage.

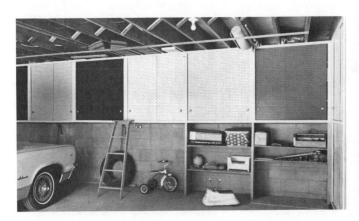

Low-headroom nooks under the eaves can be put to good use for storage. Scallop-topped "fence" above conceals a row of shelves and clothes poles. Leaving the top part open to the ceiling makes the room seem larger than if it were closed in. Tree branches painted on the wall behind give illusion of a distant garden scene to increase the feeling of space.

Sloping built-in at right packs a lot of storage in a little space, even has a drop-down desk. Side doors give access to rear compartments.

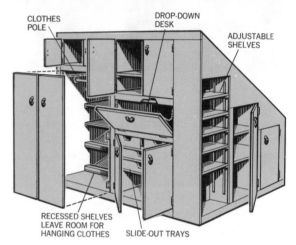

Slanted shelves in cupboard at left work like supermarket racks. Cans, stored on their sides, roll conveniently down to you as you lift the front ones out. In the center photo, shallow shelves are used in place of conventional overhead cabinets.

Cans and jars are easy to see and can be reached without necessity of removing the items from the front to get at those in back. In the cupboard at right, closely spaced shelves and vertical dividers keep thin objects such as trays, platters and flat pans neatly sorted.

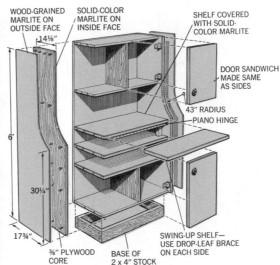

WOOD-GRAINED MARLITE ON OUTSIDE FACE

SOLID-COLOR MARLITE ON INSIDE FACE

SHELF COVERED WITH SOLID-COLOR MARLITE

DOOR SANDWICH MADE SAME AS SIDES

43" RADIUS

PIANO HINGE

14⅛"

6'

30¼"

17¾"

⅜" PLYWOOD CORE

BASE OF 2 x 4" STOCK

SWING-UP SHELF—USE DROP-LEAF BRACE ON EACH SIDE

This modern hutch stores appliances and lets you use them at the same time. Outlets at the back enable you to keep toaster, coffee maker, food blender and other electrical appliances plugged in, ready for use. A hinged panel swings up to form a serving counter. Doors and sides are a clever sandwich of ⅜-in. plywood with two kinds of paneling cemented to it—wood grained outside, solid color inside.

Storage can be handsome as well as functional. These open shelves at the foot of a stairway display decorative objects, while the larger base cabinet conceals less-showy items behind louvered doors. Such a unit not only adds storage space, but can also serve as an attractive room divider, in this case helping to screen off the stairway from a dining room.

Hollow spaces behind false walls can hide hard-to-store items like the Ping-Pong table at left, above. If you're paneling a wall, especially in a basement, it's often a good idea to leave a few inches between your framing and the old wall. This will provide room for recessed shelves, built-in stereo equipment or storage compartments such as the one here. In the wall shown, one 4-ft.-wide sheet of hardboard paneling is removable, creating a big opening so the table can easily be slipped in and out.

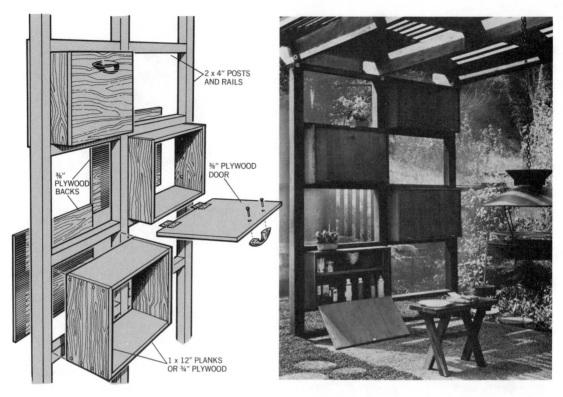

2 x 4" POSTS AND RAILS

⅜" PLYWOOD DOOR

⅜" PLYWOOD BACKS

1 x 12" PLANKS OR ¾" PLYWOOD

Wall of cabinets in a pleasing staggered arrangement gives shade and privacy and at the same time stores garden supplies, barbecue utensils and other outdoor items. Cabinets can be built under an existing structure, such as along the open side of a carport or porch, or they can be part of a garden shelter, as here. If the wall is load bearing, use 4 x 4 posts instead of 2 x 4s shown in the drawing. Note that backs of cabinets are extended to overlap posts and cross rails. This adds extra bracing and helps to strengthen the wall. Redwood is a good choice for this type of unit.

Miniature projection booth—actually an unused cellar alcove closed in with pine paneling—not only stores photo equipment out of the way, but lets you leave it set up for quick use. Swiveling projector platform holds a Super-8 projector alongside a 16-mm model so either can be run without disturbing the other. A slide and film projector could be paired in the same way.

Facing opposite ways, these over-under bunkbeds help to divide a room for youngsters of different ages and interests. On one side, lower bunk doubles as couch when area is used for teenage get-togethers. On other side, a train board drops down. Study desk swings out from the end. Celotex V-grooved panels cover bunks.

Slide-out train board goes to bed along with its owner, storing neatly away underneath. Its sloping design lets it fill the opening under the bed when pushed in for a trim appearance, while leaving the sides and back unobstructed for reaching the trains easily. Extra train equipment is kept in cupboard that forms bed's headboard.

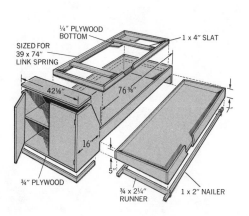

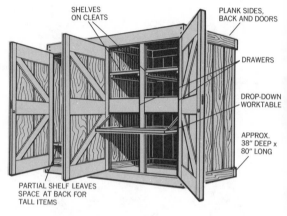

SHELVES ON CLEATS

PLANK SIDES, BACK AND DOORS

DRAWERS

DROP-DOWN WORKTABLE

APPROX. 38" DEEP x 80" LONG

PARTIAL SHELF LEAVES SPACE AT BACK FOR TALL ITEMS

Special compartments in this roomy storage unit take all the bulky things that never seem to fit anywhere—campstoves, sleeping bags, fishing-tackle boxes, ski boots, life jackets and similar outdoor gear. The tall section on the left side lets you slip skis, fishing poles, boat oars and other long items down behind a shelf where they're kept out of the way at the back. A hinged shelf swings out to provide space for working on equipment. Above this are two drawers for small items such as fishing reels and ski goggles.

A combination of perforated paneling and floor-to-ceiling poles creates this unusual storage arrangement for a playroom, den or child's bedroom. The square 2 x 2 poles, spaced about a foot away from the wall, support the front edges of shelves, while the rear edges rest on shelf brackets hooked into the paneling's holes. A small desk is also suspended between the poles. Special V-grooved hardboard paneling has perforations in upper two-thirds and is solid at bottom for a wainscot look.

Occupying no more than 6 feet of space, the island clothes sorting cabinet (above) can add a world of convenience and efficiency to a home laundry. The pretreatment sink doubles as a member of your laundry team and a clean-up area for messy fingers. The island's many drawers make it a fine companion for any washer/dryer. A wall-supported counter fitted with drawers and equipped with bar stools (upper right) provides a work/study area for the whole family. Each youngster can have his own "desk" for homework or craft activity. It's an excellent place to budget the family paycheck and plan menus. The shelf is solidly supported by protruding 2x4s anchored to wall studs. The counter is covered with laminate and each area is complete with drawer. Low-bridge areas (right) back under sloping roof of attic rooms are waiting to store countless items such as luggage, Christmas decorations, seasonal wearing apparel and the like. Standard window shutters, hinged and held shut with magnetic catches, are used to make attractive and inexpensive doors.

New look for a tired wall

■ IN A LARGE ROOM with a high ceiling, you can create a feeling of intimacy by filling the window wall from floor to ceiling and corner to corner with this bookshelf system. Visually, the change reduces the room in size and gives support to those sagging ceiling joists.

The wall system shown is based on plasterboard-covered 2x4 frames with shelving in between. For visual uniformity, the dropped soffit was built-in. The design can easily be adapted to any size wall with a little careful planning. Desk-level and floor-level shelves project slightly more than bookshelves to lessen the dominance of the vertical fins.

AN UNUSED BEDROOM was converted to a combination den/sitting room/library. This sturdy wall unit has several shelves for books and speakers, four desk-level shelves for lamp and decorations, and four floor-level shelves for the stereo receiver and more books. It makes the room feel more intimate while supporting sagging ceiling joists.

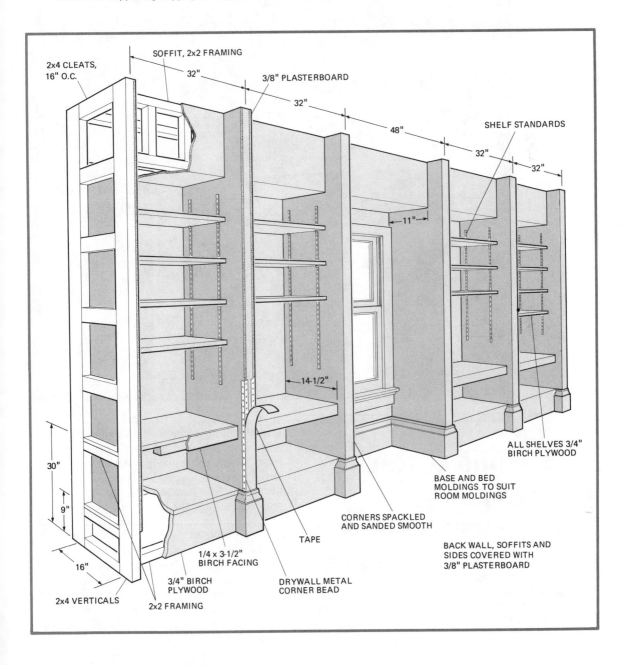

2x4 CLEATS, 16" O.C.

SOFFIT, 2x2 FRAMING

32"

3/8" PLASTERBOARD

32"

48"

SHELF STANDARDS

32"

32"

11"

14-1/2"

30"

9"

16"

2x4 VERTICALS

2x2 FRAMING

3/4" BIRCH PLYWOOD

1/4 x 3-1/2" BIRCH FACING

TAPE

DRYWALL METAL CORNER BEAD

CORNERS SPACKLED AND SANDED SMOOTH

ALL SHELVES 3/4" BIRCH PLYWOOD

BASE AND BED MOLDINGS TO SUIT ROOM MOLDINGS

BACK WALL, SOFFITS AND SIDES COVERED WITH 3/8" PLASTERBOARD

Build a stack of swingers

■ THIS ROLL-ABOUT stack of swinging trays offers handy storage for the hobbyist and the person with a home office.

The nine trays are made of ¼-in. fir plywood, butted, glued and nailed together. They swing open on a length of thinwall conduit. Use a smooth-cutting blade to mass-produce the tray parts. Use a fairly hard wood such as poplar, birch or soft maple for the tray corner blocks. Dress a square length, bevel one corner, then slice it into 3-in. pieces to project ¼ in. above the tray edges. Sand the blocks and glue in place.

Holes in the blocks must be bored squarely and identically so the trays will align and swing out evenly. Clamp a flat board to your drill-press table and two stop blocks at one corner. Hold each tray firmly against the blocks as you bore and stop when the bit's point pokes through. Turn the tray over to complete the hole. Half-inch conduit is $^{11}/_{16}$ in. o.d. (outside diameter).

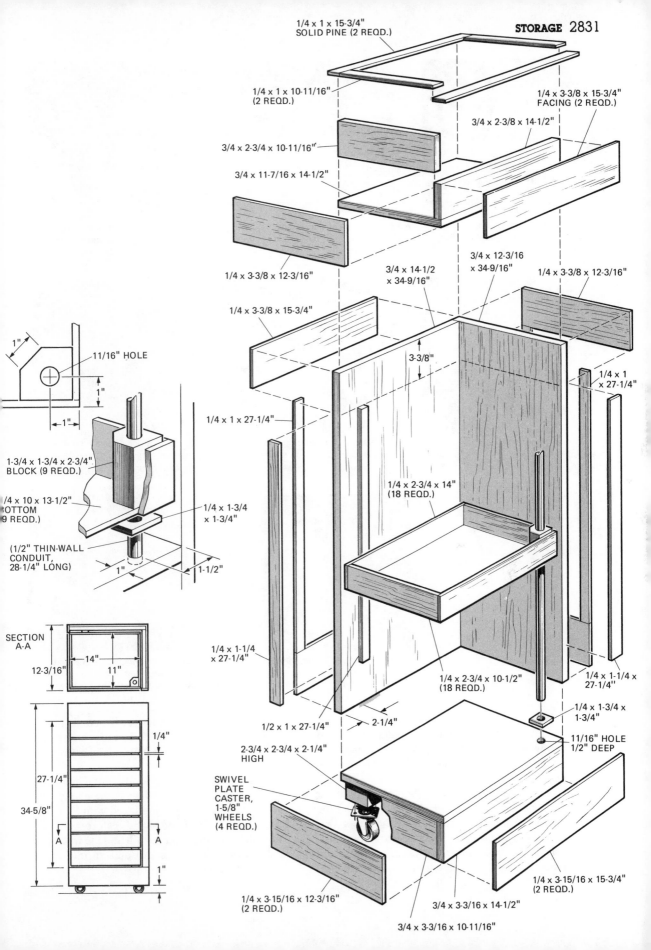

1/4 x 1 x 15-3/4"
SOLID PINE (2 REQD.)

1/4 x 1 x 10-11/16"
(2 REQD.)

1/4 x 3-3/8 x 15-3/4"
FACING (2 REQD.)

3/4 x 2-3/8 x 14-1/2"

3/4 x 2-3/4 x 10-11/16"

3/4 x 11-7/16 x 14-1/2"

1/4 x 3-3/8 x 12-3/16"

3/4 x 14-1/2
x 34-9/16"

3/4 x 12-3/16
x 34-9/16"

1/4 x 3-3/8 x 12-3/16"

1/4 x 3-3/8 x 15-3/4"

3-3/8"

1/4 x 1
x 27-1/4"

1/4 x 1 x 27-1/4"

1/4 x 2-3/4 x 14"
(18 REQD.)

1"

11/16" HOLE

1"

1"

1-3/4 x 1-3/4 x 2-3/4"
BLOCK (9 REQD.)

1/4 x 10 x 13-1/2"
BOTTOM
(9 REQD.)

(1/2" THIN-WALL
CONDUIT,
28-1/4" LONG)

1/4 x 1-3/4
x 1-3/4"

1"

1-1/2"

1/4 x 1-1/4
x 27-1/4"

1/4 x 2-3/4 x 10-1/2"
(18 REQD.)

1/4 x 1-1/4 x
27-1/4"

1/4 x 1-3/4 x
1-3/4"

SECTION
A-A

14"

11"

12-3/16"

1/4"

27-1/4"

34-5/8"

A   A

1"

1/2 x 1 x 27-1/4"

2-1/4"

2-3/4 x 2-3/4 x 2-1/4"
HIGH

SWIVEL
PLATE
CASTER,
1-5/8"
WHEELS
(4 REQD.)

11/16" HOLE
1/2" DEEP

1/4 x 3-15/16 x 15-3/4"
(2 REQD.)

1/4 x 3-15/16 x 12-3/16"
(2 REQD.)

3/4 x 3-3/16 x 14-1/2"

3/4 x 3-3/16 x 10-11/16"

ASSEMBLE trays with glue and ⅝-in. (20-ga.) brads, being careful to drive them straight. Cut parts from flat plywood.

EASE all sharp corners of assembled trays with a block plane, then sand outside surfaces.

PROTECT outside corner with a notched 90° block when gluing and clamping pivot blocks in right front corners of trays.

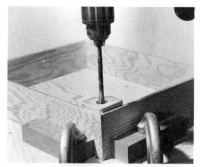

CLAMP two stop blocks to wood drill-press table to assure identically bored holes in the corner blocks of all nine trays.

COAT HOLES with sanding sealer, then sand when dry. Cotton on stick makes swab. Follow with candle wax.

SLIDE TRAYS over conduit post. Wax coating inside holes and on tops of corner blocks assures smooth-swinging trays.

BORE HOLES for conduit in top and bottom sections of cabinet before final assembly. Glue the bottom section first.

ATTACH free-swinging, swivel plate casters to the four corner blocks. Wheels should extend about 1 in. below sides.

When the holes are bored, paint trays and insides of holes with sanding sealer, then sand lightly when dry with 220-grit paper, holes and all. Rub a wax candle in the holes and across the tops of the blocks.

Make the outer cabinet shell from ¾-in. fir plywood. Drill a ¼-in.-deep hole in the top of the base section and in underside of the upper section, and nail and glue the base section in position. Insert the conduit in the hole in the base and place the upper section over the top of the conduit. Then glue and nail the top section in place.

Now turn the unit upside down and install blocks in the corners for plate-type swivel casters.

A facing of ¼-in. plywood is attached to all surfaces except the top edges of the upper compartment. These edges are faced with ¼ x 1-in. solid pine. Ease (round slightly) all corners with a block plane and sand. You'll find the wild grain pattern of fir plywood can add an interesting effect when finished natural.

Putting green from artificial turf

■ IF YOU'D RATHER spend Saturdays swinging a putter than a grass whip, synthetic turf can make your dreams come true. The decorative "carpet" has a fiber facing that closely resembles living grass both in appearance and feel. The beauty of it is that once it is installed, there's no maintenance. It is made of second-generation polypropylene, polymerized to withstand aging and the weathering of extreme outdoor conditions. Synthetic turf is sold nationally through carpet dealers and building-supply centers that also stock installation materials. Ask their advice regarding installation in your area.

The turf can be installed professionally or by a do-it-yourselfer. Since the carpet comes in 6 and 12-ft. widths, the putting greens shown here are designed to utilize those modules.

The dirt or soil subsurface of the area to be covered should be shaped and well tamped. The manufacturer recommends either 1½ in. of asphalt or concrete over the compacted base for the synthetic turf to adhere to. (This minimum thickness will vary with load requirements.) Installation directly over earth is not recommended.

The surface finish should be as smooth and nonporous as possible. Because of the latter requirement, the covered area should be pitched slightly to direct water runoff where you want it to go.

The perimeter boards (headers) can be installed as shown in the drawings or as in the photo below. The latter method creates shiplap joints by doubling up two-bys. Start by installing the headers because these can also be used for screeding the concrete. Once they are in and secured by stakes, the earth inside can be excavated and tamped. Then the concrete is laid up to the

solid header and maintained approximately ⅜ to ½ in. below the header's top edge. This measurement should be as consistent as possible to maintain a uniform grass height. You can achieve it by using a notched screed on the header boards to level the concrete. If you use asphalt instead of concrete, seal the surface and allow it to dry overnight before installing the turf.

Sweep the surface clean and patch any irregularities. Spread the synthetic turf in the sun to warm it and trim the edges to be butted. Then, using a 3/32-in. notched trowel, spread adhesive over the area of exposed width. When the adhesive barely transfers to your finger (10 to 20 minutes), the turf can be rolled onto the surface. You can assure invisible seams with tape. This is positioned astraddle the edge. The grass is simply tapped into place with a hammer.

The turf and related material—flags, cups and instructions—come as a kit. Simply select the layout you want and order the amount of carpeting in the kit.

In addition to a putting green, you might want to consider the synthetic turf for swimming-pool aprons, patios, roof decks and the like. It's comfortable to walk on and durable.

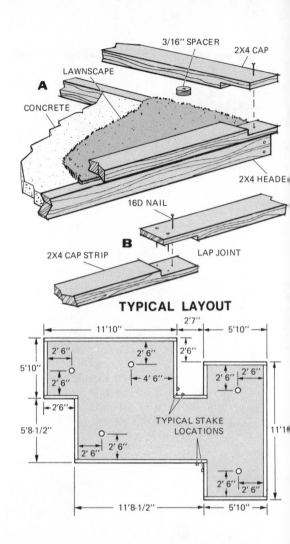

TYPICAL LAYOUT

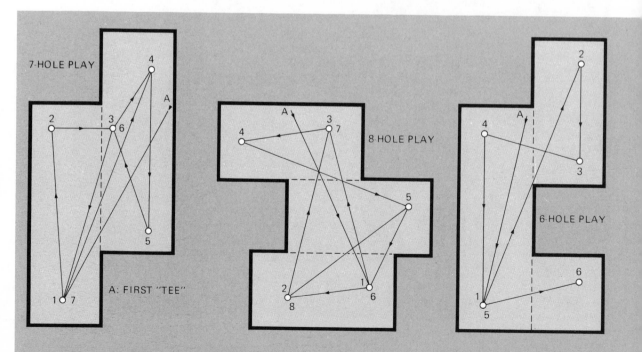

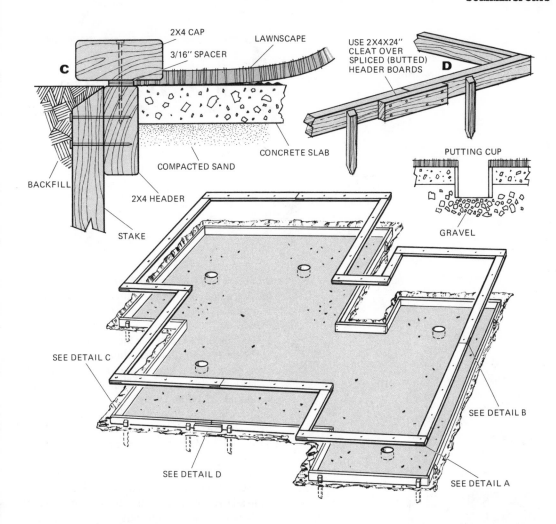

2X4 CAP

LAWNSCAPE

3/16" SPACER

C

USE 2X4X24"
CLEAT OVER
SPLICED (BUTTED)
HEADER BOARDS

D

CONCRETE SLAB

COMPACTED SAND

BACKFILL

2X4 HEADER

STAKE

PUTTING CUP

GRAVEL

SEE DETAIL C

SEE DETAIL B

SEE DETAIL D

SEE DETAIL A

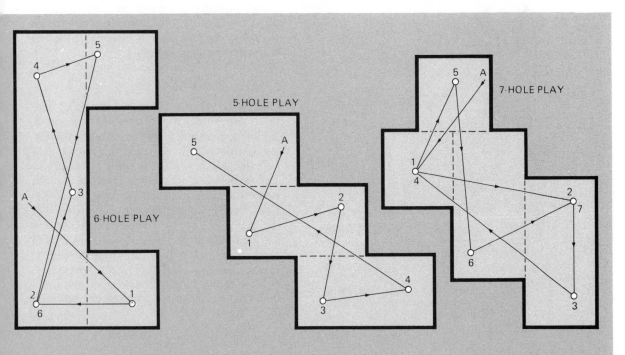

6·HOLE PLAY

5·HOLE PLAY

7·HOLE PLAY

Go fly a kite

■ YOU HAVEN'T really flown a kite until you have graduated from the standard store-bought two-stick jobs and tried one of the more exotic fliers.

It is true that experts call the two-stick kite one of the best all-around fliers, but from an esthetic standpoint, it can't begin to compete with such marvelous oddities as the Japanese bird or delta wing kites. So if you want to become the center of attraction at your local park, or see your prestige zoom skyward in the eyes of your children, try one of the designs illustrated on the following pages.

You can now buy an amazing variety of kites at kite stores—places that specialize in kites from all over the world—but kite making is easy, so there is no need to buy one. The materials are readily available. Assembly takes only a couple of hours at most. And your personal design variations can produce a flier that may be better than anything you might buy.

Making your kites

Materials. Kite-making materials fall into three categories: sticks, coverings and glue. Sticks, of course, are used to make the frames, and small wood slats are the most common stick material. The best are of white pine or spruce. Yellow pine and fir are not too good for this purpose because they tend to snap too easily. Balsa wood is wonderfully light but is altogether too fragile for kite use. Many kite makers today use hardwood dowels, ranging in size from ⅛ to ⅜-in. in dia. Oriental kites are made of strips of rattan or bamboo. Any store which carries materials for caning chairs will have rattan, and you'll find bamboo at places which sell bamboo window shades.

THE PLANS for this sled kite are shown at the top of the following page. It has no horizontal struts and depends entirely on wind pressure to remain open in flight.

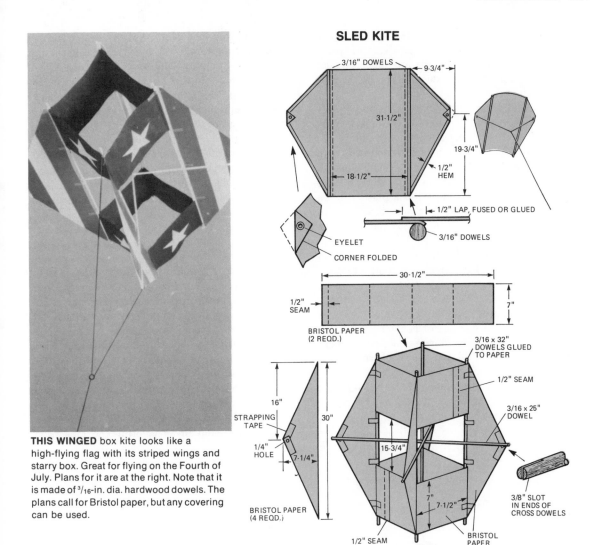

SLED KITE

WINGED BOX KITE

THIS WINGED box kite looks like a high-flying flag with its striped wings and starry box. Great for flying on the Fourth of July. Plans for it are at the right. Note that it is made of 3/16-in. dia. hardwood dowels. The plans call for Bristol paper, but any covering can be used.

Coverings for kites are of three types—paper, cloth and plastic. Many a successful kite has been covered with last week's newspapers, though if you are shooting for durability, newspapers aren't the best route. Brown kraft wrapping paper is stronger. Japanese rice paper, available at art supply stores, is an old standby in the kite trade, but it is a little heavy. Probably the best compromise between strength and weight is Madras tissue, an oriental tissue paper likely to be found in stores which sell oriental goods.

Cloth coverings include ordinary muslin, cambric, silk and lightweight nylon spinnaker cloth. Think about using a cloth covering on high fliers such as box kites, which need the strength of cloth and can carry the weight. Plastic coverings include polyethylene—the stuff of which plastic garbage bags are made—and mylar polyester. You'll find the latter at most paint stores, sold in big sheets for use as dropcloths. It is light and very inexpensive.

You'll need adhesives to attach the coverings to the frame. Ordinary paper paste was the standby for years, and still works on paper kites. Modern quick-drying white glues are probably better, and they work on cloth as well as paper. Rubber cement and contact cement are good. Just remember that to get a good bond with rubber cement you must coat both pieces, allow the cement to dry, and then press the surfaces together. When you coat just one surface, you get a weak bond. If you are working with plastic, you'll need a cement which works on the particular plastic you have. Check the glue counter at your hardware store.

You'll find use for adhesive tapes, too, in kite making. Clear cellophane tape is fine for many jobs. If you need real strength, use one of the packaging tapes, which are reinforced with fibers. For cloth kites, iron-on tapes are good for making seams and joining pieces of cloth. For the lightest of all seam joiners, use a plastic ribbon which, when placed between two pieces of cloth and heated with an iron, bonds the pieces of cloth.

Once your kite is built, you'll need a line on which to fly it. The experts say that wrapping twine is too heavy and regular string is too fuzzy. (The wind catches the fuzz and creates too much drag.) They recommend, for very light kites, carpet thread of 12/4 size. For heavier kites, think about fish line. You can buy nylon monofilament line in a variety of thicknesses. Furthermore, fish lines are rated by the weight they can carry, which is convenient for kite fliers. A 28-lb. test line is fine for medium-sized kites, and for bigger models, the line can range upward to about an 80-lb. test.

When you really get into the spirit of kite making, you turn artistic and become concerned with the appearance of your creations as well as their flying ability. The winged box kite shown, done in red, white and blue, for example, is great for patriotic occasions such as the Fourth of July. And the highly imaginative bird and face kites are typical of the artistry put into their kites by the Japanese, who probably have been flying kites longer than anyone else around.

Most of the drawings of kites on these pages are self-explanatory. Follow the dimensions shown for making the frame, and then cover it as shown, using the materials of your choice. About the only trick you need to know is that the best way to join two sticks in frame making is to wrap the joint with fairly heavy thread and then soak the thread with white glue. When the glue sets, you'll have a very strong joint. You can drive staples or brads through these joints, but when you do, you run the risk of splitting the stick.

Sometimes, the biggest problem is finding material to make the tail. Most kites need some kind of a tail, and the standard tail for years has been strips of sheeting tied together, but it costs money to tear up sheeting. Kite fliers have found a neat substitute: They buy rolls of crepe paper—the kind used to decorate gymnasiums for homecoming games—and make colorful kite tails from them.

DELTA WING KITE

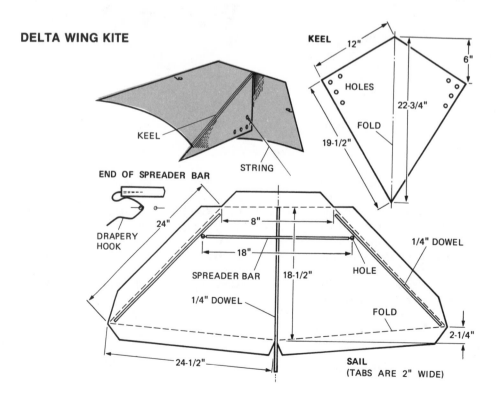

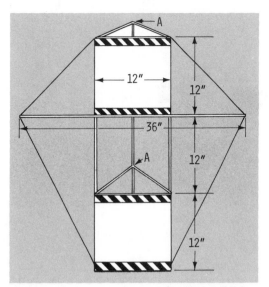

AFTER COVERING this kite's top and bottom (leaving center open), form bat-wing's outline with string and cover it separately. Attach the bridle at point A. The diagram below shows how the rudder version is controlled by lines from the ground.

FLEXIBLE KITE

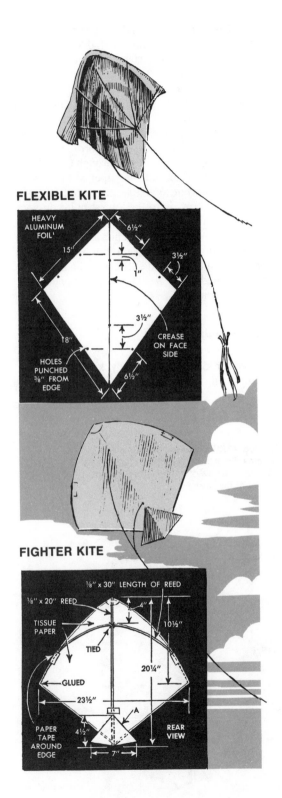

FIGHTER KITE

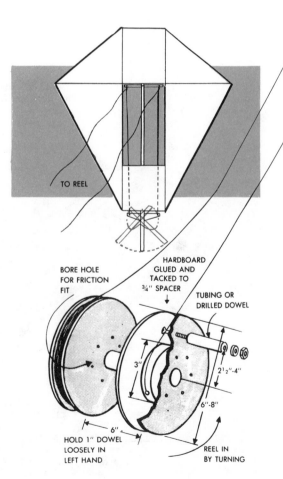

Keep in mind when making a kite tail that it is not the weight of the tail which does the work, but the bulk and the surface which provide balance. The stronger the wind, the more tail needed. Some kites, such as the box variety, don't need tails, but most do, particularly on very windy days.

You can make an unusual tail by folding sheets of typing paper so they are accordion-pleated. After folding, drive a staple through the folds at the center and fan out the paper at both ends. This makes what looks like a pleated bow tie. Attach this bow tie to the lowest point on your kite, using a string about 1 ft. long. Use as many bow ties as necessary to achieve balance, tying each additional bow about a foot below the last one. You'll be pleased at the way the kite looks as it flies high in the wind with a string of bow ties riding beneath.

Flying your kites

Most people think that a very windy day is required for kite flying. Actually, kites fly best in a light, steady breeze of from 8 to 15 mph. Have a

IN THIS MANEUVERABLE VERSION of the triangular box kite, the frame dimensions differ from those given for the conventional type, but the main feature of the maneuverable design is the fish-tail rudder at the rear.

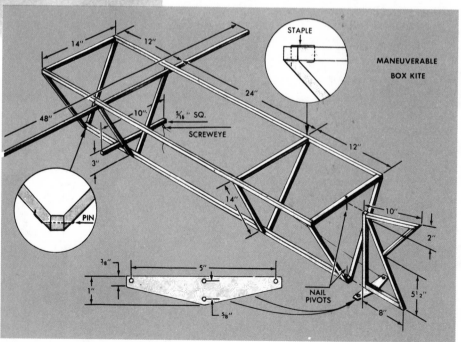

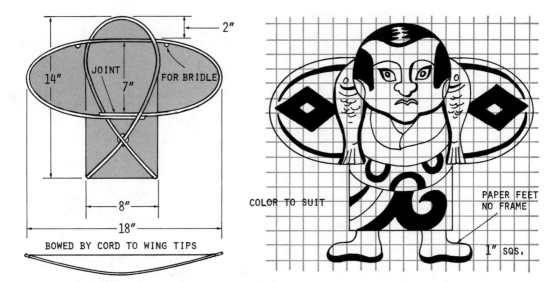

COLOR TO SUIT

JOINT 7"

14"

2"

FOR BRIDLE

8"

18"

BOWED BY CORD TO WING TIPS

PAPER FEET
NO FRAME

1" SQS.

NIKKO KITE

helper stand downwind, 50 to 100 feet away from you, raise the kite until it is lifted by the wind, and then lightly toss it straight up. At the same time, you should pull *lightly* on the string.

The kite should begin to climb steadily, and as it climbs, you should pay out string at a rate that allows it to keep climbing. If you pay it out too fast, the kite may stagger in the air and fall. To recover control when this happens, pull in the excess string until the kite starts to climb again,

and then begin paying out once more—but at a slower rate.

A well-balanced kite should climb with no problems in any light breeze; if your kite doesn't, you can assume that it is too heavy for its surface area, so it can't develop the necessary lift.

The bridle is important in flying a kite. It is usually attached to two or more points of the frame, depending on the kite design, and the flying string is tied to it. Kites fly best when the

THIS HIGH SAILER is a triangular box with wings which are bowed to give them dihedral. Note the pattern for the covering of the top of the kite. Use a lightweight cloth such as cambric or organdy.

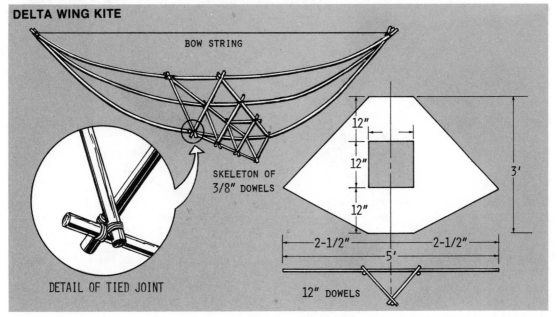

DELTA WING KITE

BOW STRING

SKELETON OF
3/8" DOWELS

DETAIL OF TIED JOINT

12"

12"

12"

3'

2-1/2"   2-1/2"

5'

12" DOWELS

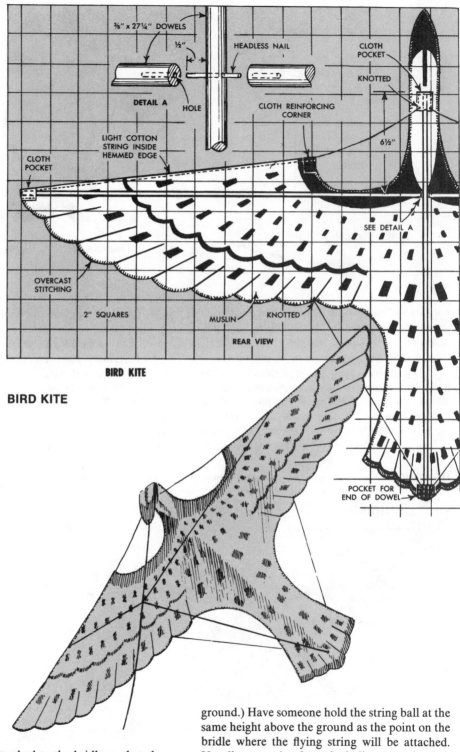

BIRD KITE

BIRD KITE

flying string is attached to the bridle so that the kite is at an angle of 30 to 40 degrees. An easy way to determine the angle is to set the kite upright on the ground and then tilt it forward about 30 degrees. (This is about ⅓ of the way to the ground.) Have someone hold the string ball at the same height above the ground as the point on the bridle where the flying string will be attached. Unroll some string from the ball and see that it is parallel to the ground. Tie it to the bridle with the kite still in the tilted position. Tie a tight knot so the flying string will not slide on the bridle, and the kite is ready to fly.

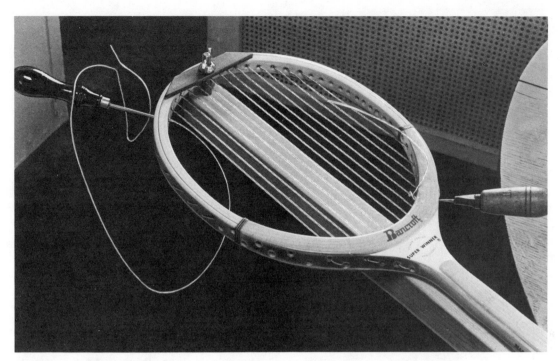

SIMPLE JIG for holding racket is length of wood and clamps, turns table into rig for racket repairs.

Restring your own tennis racket

■ IT'S SATURDAY MORNING and during a warm-up rally you pop a string on your favorite racket. No need to give up the weekend matches or play with an uncomfortable borrowed racket. If your restringing and repair shop is closed or miles away, try some of these simple shortcuts.

A very small investment can provide you with a jig to hold the racket and materials for restringing and replacing your grip as well.

Materials you will need for the method shown here are simply a three-foot length of 1½x1½ stock, preferably hardwood, and an eight-inch length of 1½-inch dowel (like that on which rugs are sometimes delivered) that you will cushion with a wrap of leather or adhesive tape. Also needed are two three-inch or four-inch "C" clamps to hold the wood base and your racket to your workbench or kitchen table plus a four-inch ⅜-16 NC hold-down bolt with wingnut to secure the head of the racket, and some scraps of hardwood so the clamps don't scratch your racket handle. A couple of awls from a hardware store will hold the string in place.

You can buy nylon string in a 35-foot length from your tennis shop or mail-order supplier. Nylon lasts several times longer than gut and is much easier to work with.

Threading the main strings

Clamp down your racket, as shown, with the side grooves slanting down and toward the head of the racket. All strings always go into the lower hole and out the upper hole of the groove. Starting with the main strings, the vertical ones, cut a 19-foot length of nylon and thread it through the two top holes so that half (9½ feet) goes on each side of the center-post bolt holding the racket head. The bolt is filed flat on each side to protect strings from damage. Thread these main strings down through the first holes on each side of the neck.

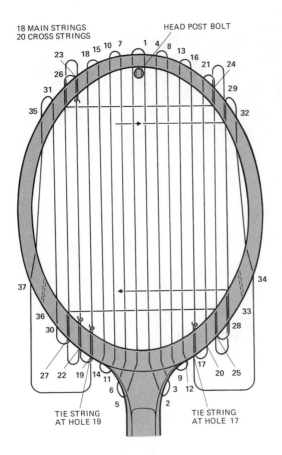

18 MAIN STRINGS
20 CROSS STRINGS
HEAD POST BOLT

TIE STRING
AT HOLE 19

TIE STRING
AT HOLE 17

Sight through these holes to see their direction and then carefully but firmly insert one awl into No. 1 to hold the string in place. Wrap the string coming out hole No. 2 one and a half turns around the string-tightening dowel handle and, using the frame for leverage, turn to tension the string. Be sure the string coming out is straight so you are not tightening against added friction. Insert the second awl in hole No. 2 and remove the tightening handle. Thread the string through holes 3 and 4, tighten, and insert the awl in hole 4. Repeat procedure on the other side through holes 5,6,7. Awls are now in holes 4 and 7.

Continue this threading and tightening process alternately in numerical order, as shown, until there are 16 strings threaded and awls are in holes 29 and 31. Strumming each string as it is tightened will give you an indication of proper tension. Thread 32 and 34, then 35 and 37, being careful to skip holes 33 and 36. Pull strings extra tight, insert awls, rethread those loose ends through holes 17 and 19, and tie off each with a simple half hitch. If the nylon is slippery, add an extra half hitch; then cut off excess string ¼-inch from the knot.

Threading the cross strings

Cross strings are threaded from the remaining 16-foot length. If hole 22 is a top hole, thread one end up through and half hitch to the main string there. If a bottom hole, No. 20 on the other side must be used instead. Thread the other end through hole 27 and weave under and over the main vertical strings over to and through hole 25 on the opposite side. Tighten, insert awl and continue weaving across and up the racket until 20 cross strings have been strung. The 20th string goes through hole 26, is tightened, threaded through hole 23 and then tied to the main string there and cut off. During cross-string threading when a main string already occupies a hole, it's helpful to sharpen the tip of the cross string; snip it off diagonally to a point.

Now go over the racket with a slim dowel or pencil (since your awl might cut into a string) and straighten those strings out of line so that they all cross at right angles and are parallel.

Replacing the grip

Grip replacement is also not too difficult—once you know how. Remove the old grip, and coat the handle with mucilage or shellac. Air until tacky. With a ⅜-inch flat-headed nail, secure the tapered end of the grip strip flush with the butt end of the handle, nailing through ¼ inch from the end of the leather. Hold the racket head between your legs and wrap the grip flush around the butt end and then on down the handle clockwise with the leather layers butting or slightly overlapping, if so designed. Tack the finished end with a ⅜-inch nail, trim off excess leather with a razor, and cover the nail and edge with two or three turns of ½-inch plastic tape.

Restringing with gut

Gut restringing can be attempted after you have become proficient with nylon. Because of gut's reaction to moisture (a rain shower can ruin its tension), it should be treated with preservative after stringing and occasionally during active use after exposure to damp conditions or when the strings are becoming slightly frayed.

Mix one part of white three-pound cut absolute shellac with five parts of water-free ethanol in an 8-ounce salad dressing jar with screw top. Store a ¾-inch brush with cutdown handle inside the jar. When strings are frayed or damp, just dry with talc or a fluffy towel, then paint on a light coat. Thin mixture with alcohol from time to time. Too thick a coat or too frequent use makes gut strings lose resiliency. Never use it on any type of nylon strings.

The stringing method outlined here can also be used with all metal rackets except the Wilson Steel and Seamco Aluminum. The rig works as well with squash, paddle and badminton rackets, although badminton strings are 19-gauge and much thinner.

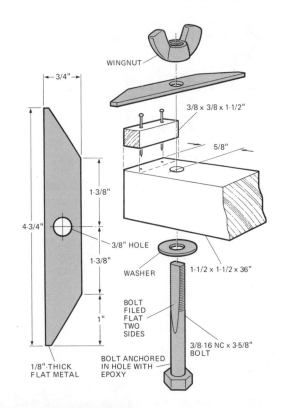

- WINGNUT
- 3/8 × 3/8 × 1-1/2"
- 3/4"
- 5/8"
- 4-3/4"
- 1-3/8"
- 3/8" HOLE
- WASHER
- 1-3/8"
- 1-1/2 × 1-1/2 × 36"
- BOLT FILED FLAT TWO SIDES
- 1"
- 3/8-16 NC × 3-5/8" BOLT
- 1/8"-THICK FLAT METAL
- BOLT ANCHORED IN HOLE WITH EPOXY

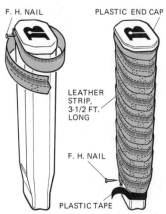

- F. H. NAIL
- PLASTIC END CAP
- LEATHER STRIP, 3-1/2 FT. LONG
- F. H. NAIL
- PLASTIC TAPE

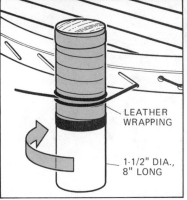

- LEATHER WRAPPING
- 1-1/2" DIA., 8" LONG

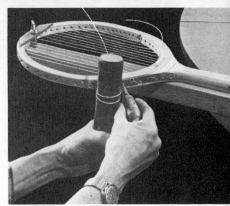

RACKET JIG (at upper right) uses bolt cap to hold the head of racket plus C-clamps to secure a brace to the table. Renewing grip (above) starts with a leather strip 3½ feet long which is stretch-wrapped down the handle and finally secured with a nail and a plastic tape ring.

TENSIONING OF NEW STRINGS (right) is done with a 1½-inch-thick dowel with leather or adhesive wrap. The string is looped around the handle and is turned to tighten, held with an awl while the next length is laced in place. Cross strings weave under and over the main strings.

Steering and suspension systems service

■ WHEN CAR OWNERS get together to trade complaints, one topic that always turns up is suspension problems. The usual problems are shimmy (vibration) and wheel tramp conditions. Noisy steering is also a frequent complaint, followed by problems with shock absorbers, springs, front-end alignment and wheel bearings.

Some suspension problems are better left to professionals, but you can frequently diagnose problems yourself. In some cases the cure may be as simple as inflating your tires to the proper pressure. Here are some tips on running down suspension and steering problems.

Shaking things up

The terms shimmy, vibration and quiver are synonymous. None, however, is the same as wheel tramp (thump).

Shimmy is the continuous shaking sensation you feel in the steering wheel (most often), floor or seat while driving on a paved highway at a set speed usually between 50 and 70 mph. It continues as long as you maintain that speed, but disappears or diminishes when the speed is increased or decreased.

Front-wheel tramp is a cyclical thumping sensation that's transmitted through the steering wheel, floor or seat at a speed of about 25 mph.

Some malfunctions that cause vibration may also cause wheel tramp, but usually what creates one sensation will not produce the other.

Wheel and tire unbalance is often blamed for vibration, and yet it's just one of 11 possible reasons—not even the most common. Here's a list of all usual causes of vibration. An asterisk means that the particular condition should be tackled before others since testing is easier and can be made without cost:

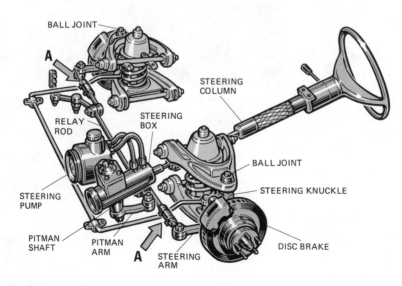

BALL JOINT

A

STEERING COLUMN

RELAY ROD

STEERING BOX

STEERING PUMP

BALL JOINT

STEERING KNUCKLE

PITMAN SHAFT

PITMAN ARM

A

STEERING ARM

DISC BRAKE

STEERING LINKAGE can be tested for looseness at tie-rod adjustment sleeves (A).

- Improper tire pressure*
- Tire bulge*
- Loose wheel nuts*
- Worn shock absorbers*
- Loose steering linkage*
- Worn or loose front wheel bearings*
- Loose engine mount*
- Incorrect driveshaft angularity*
- Worn ball joints
- Unbalanced wheel and tire assemblies
- Improper front-end alignment

Eliminating shimmy

Use these procedures to eliminate shimmy:

1. See that tire pressure is neither low nor uneven, and examine tire sidewalls for bulges that can cause shimmy. Discard a bulging tire—it's unsafe.

2. Tighten wheel nuts with a hand wrench, preferably a torque wrench, to manufacturer specification. Tighten nuts in a crisscross manner to equalize pressure around the wheel. Tighten each nut, in turn, to half its torque value—then go back and tighten each to full value.

Caution: Avoid having wheel nuts tightened with pneumatic power wrenches, which can enlarge wheelnut holes, preventing nuts from securing the wheel. This would cause the wheel to wobble. Pneumatic tools can also distort brake drums and discs.

3. Test shock absorbers by pushing up and down on the bumper or fender at each corner of the car in turn. Increase the length of the stroke with each push until the car is rocking really well. Then release your grasp on the bumper or fender at the bottom of a downstroke. If the car continues to rock up and down two or more times, the shock absorber in that corner is probably worn and should be removed from the car for further testing. Replace if necessary.

Other ways of discovering a bad shock include examining the shock's case for fluid. A leaking shock absorber should be replaced. You should also grasp each shock and try shaking it. If the shock is loose, tighten fasteners and retest. If still loose, the bushing is probably worn and should be replaced, if possible. If not, replace the shock.

Important: If one shock absorber has to be replaced, replace the other shock on the same axle. It is not necessary, however, to replace shocks at the other end of the car, assuming both are still in good condition.

4. Examine steering linkage, consisting of tie rods, pitman arm, idler arm and relay rod. Look for bent components. Grasp each and try shaking. If any rod is bent and/or demonstrates looseness, replace that part. A damaged or worn steering linkage component results in vibration and also loose steering control, jerky steering and side-to-side wander of the car.

5. To determine if front wheel bearings are causing vibration, feel wheels or hubcaps after driving the car several miles. Friction could heat the wheels, signifying a worn or improperly adjusted wheel bearing. You should also jack up the front of the car and spin each wheel by hand.

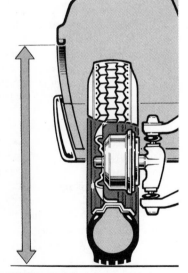

WEAK or broken springs can be detected by comparing height of sides.

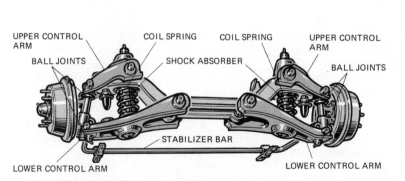

UPPER CONTROL ARM   COIL SPRING   COIL SPRING   UPPER CONTROL ARM

BALL JOINTS   SHOCK ABSORBER   BALL JOINTS

STABILIZER BAR

LOWER CONTROL ARM   LOWER CONTROL ARM

FRONT SUSPENSION components for typical rear-wheel drive car are shown here.

If you hear clicking, grinding or scraping, remove the wheel, inspect bearings for damage, and adjust bearings properly before replacing the wheel.

Important: With cars having frontwheel drive only, inspect rear wheel bearings as described. If a vehicle is equipped with both front and rear-wheel drive (that is, four-wheel drive), the inspection is unnecessary. Wheel bearings on an axle with a drive system seldom fail because they are being treated constantly with lubricant from the differential or transfer case.

6. One of the most serious conditions that causes vibration is a loose engine mount. Reports have reached us of mounts loosening so badly that engines have actually rocked forward, smashing radiators. In more severe cases, loosened engine mounts have caused throttles to jam, leading to runaway cars.

At the first indication of shimmy, engine mounts should be tested. Vibration is the initial indication of looseness.

If a car has a manual transmission, let the engine idle. Set the hand brake tightly, place the transmission in gear and have someone let the clutch out. If an engine mount is loose or defective, the engine will give a violent upward jerk as it stalls out.

If the car is equipped with automatic transmission, place a hydraulic jack under the oil pan or some other accessible section of the engine block. Put a 2x4 wood block between the jack and engine to prevent damage, and lift up carefully on the engine. If the engine mount is loose, the engine will lift far enough off the mount for you to see daylight between the two.

Caution: Don't put too much pressure on the oil pan. You may cause damage.

If an engine mount is loose, it should be tightened with a torque wrench to manufacturer specification. If damaged, or if it won't tighten up, it should be replaced.

7. Check universal joints as discussed in the section on transmission and drive train. With the car on a two-post lift so wheels hang free and the driveshaft is not obstructed, have someone start the engine and place the transmission in gear as you watch the action of the driveshaft.

Driveshaft motion should be smooth. If the shaft is out of alignment, it will whip. Edges of the shaft will look blurry.

Wash the shaft with cleaning solvent on the chance that a cake of mud or some other foreign matter is throwing the shaft out of balance. Look for damage to the shaft. A shaft that's bent or dented should be replaced.

Now, bring the car down to the ground. See that it's resting on level pavement and measure the distance from the ground to the center of the fender well with a gauge. Do this at each corner of the car. You are looking for a weak or broken spring that can cause a driveshaft to whip during driving. If one corner measures lower than the opposing corner, the existence of a bad spring is verified. This procedure can also be used to check for weak springs.

If shimmy still exists after other possible causes have been investigated, have driveshaft angularity checked. Angularity has to be determined with a driveshaft alignment gauge against manufacturer specification.

8. Have ball joints tested for axial (up-and-down) movement. This is done by jacking up each front wheel, relieving pressure on the load-bearing joint, attaching a dial indicator to the wheel assembly and prying up on the wheel assembly. See if movement falls within manufacturer requirements. If it exceeds this specification, ball joints should be replaced.

Ball joints in some cars since 1974 (GM in particular) have indicators that allow you to make this check yourself. Just wipe off the base of the joint and scrape a screwdriver or your fingernail across it. If you can feel a nub, the ball joint is not worn beyond limits. If you can't, replace the joint.

9. If vibration started right after you put new tires on the car, replaced a brake drum or disc, rotated tires, or upset the original setting of wheel assemblies in some way, have wheel assembly balance tested dynamically and statically—that is, with wheel assemblies in motion and at rest, respectively. Correct an unbalanced condition with balancing weights.

10. Finally, a misaligned front end may be causing the vibration, and the car's camber, caster and toe should be checked against manufacturer specification and corrected. Besides vibration, front-end misalignment can cause pulling of the car to one side on a level roadway when you remove your hands from the steering wheel, instability (wander and weaving), tire squeal on turns and uneven tire wear.

Wheel tramp

There are only three reasons for wheel tramp—weak shock absorbers, unbalanced wheel assemblies and out-of-round tires. We've discussed how to check out the first two.

To verify the existence of an out-of-round tire, inflate all tires to 50 pounds and drive the car. If a tire is causing tramp, you will not feel the sensation. To uncover the offender, reduce inflation in one tire to normal pressure and drive the car. Follow the procedure for each of the tires until tramp reappears, revealing the eccentric tire.

Steering problems

Other than vibration already discussed, the most common complaint relative to steering is noise when the steering wheel is turned sharply.

Start by seeing to it that the power-steering-pump drive belt is properly tightened. Loose drive belts cause more power steering difficulties, including noise, than anything else. Noise may also be caused by a glazed belt or pump pulley.

If noise continues, the job becomes one for a steering technician. The noise may not be coming from the booster, but from the steering itself. Maybe the cross shaft has to be adjusted or is damaged.

Another frequent steering-related complaint is a rattle which seems to be coming from the steering wheel itself. This is most frequently caused by a worn or loose steering column coupling. To test for this condition, give the steering wheel a couple of good shakes while the car is at rest. If the noise occurs, check out the coupling. Either tighten it to manufacturer specification or, if worn, replace it.

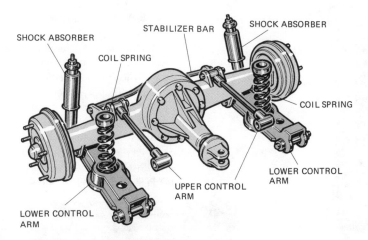

REAR SUSPENSION may be of the coil-spring type (shown here) or the leaf-spring.

Shock absorbers

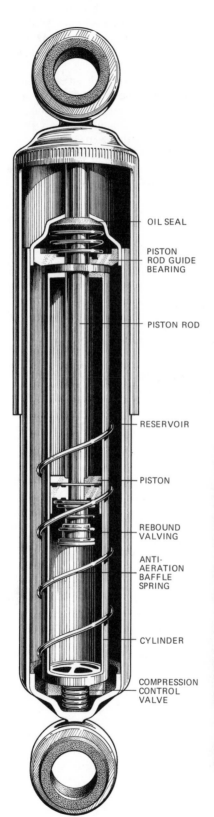

OIL SEAL

PISTON
ROD GUIDE
BEARING

PISTON ROD

RESERVOIR

PISTON

REBOUND
VALVING

ANTI-
AERATION
BAFFLE
SPRING

CYLINDER

COMPRESSION
CONTROL
VALVE

■ SHOCK ABSORBERS are often taken for granted. Yet these relatively simple little devices are vital to your safety and comfort. Poor shocks cause a rough ride and sloppy road handling. Bad shocks can be downright dangerous. Fortunately, failing shocks are comparatively easy to detect and replace.

Oddly enough, shock absorbers do not themselves absorb shock—they control the action of your car's springs, which in turn absorb road shock. Without shocks, your springs would not function properly.

Technically, shocks are direct-acting, velocity-sensitive dampening devices—direct-acting because they're mounted directly between a car's frame and axle; velocity-sensitive because the faster they move, the more resistance they offer. As the speed of a typical shock is increased on a shock-absorber dynamometer from 30 to 85 to 170 cycles per minute, control on rebound (extension) increases from 165 to 285 to 430 pounds, respectively. Control on compression (jounce)

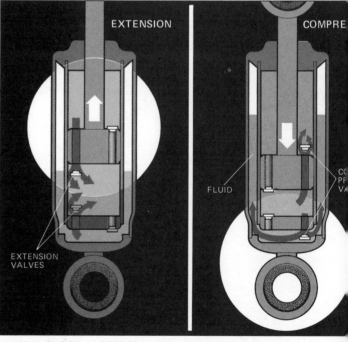

EXTENSION

COMPRE

FLUID

EXTENSION
VALVES

TYPICAL SHOCK ABSORBER (left) contains hydraulic fluid that quickly da the continuous up-and-down motion of a car on its springs. System of valve trols flow of the fluid through compression and extension cycles.

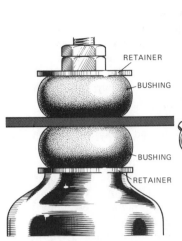

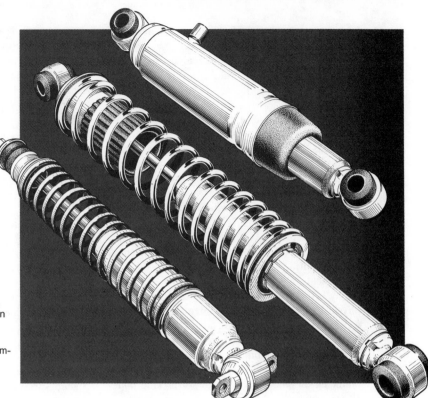

LOAD-CARRYING SHOCKS combine springs with shock absorber. The left shock (at right) is a front-load carrier, center is a rear-load carrier, right is an air-adjustable shock. Drawing shows stud-type mounting. Tighten nut only until bushing spreads to the same diameter as retainer.

increases from 60 to 185 to 275 pounds, respectively. Greater extension control is needed to compensate for the more powerful springing action that takes place during rebound.

The term "dampening" refers to the fact that shocks dampen, or restrict, the action of a vehicle's springs. If there were no shock absorbers, springs would bounce and rebound freely, making steering difficult, causing wheels to lift off the road, reducing braking efficiency and shaking up the car's passengers.

Convert motion to heat

Shock absorbers convert mechanical energy of up and down motion into a heat energy that is dissipated through the shock. The principles of fluid displacement are employed.

During compression, the piston rod and piston move down in the working cylinder, which causes a pressure drop in the upper part of the cylinder. The volume of the lower part is reduced.

Path of least resistance

To correct the pressure imbalance, hydraulic fluid follows the path of least resistance. This route is up through the upper compression valve, which is unseated by the force of the fluid. Thus the upper part of the cylinder is filled.

However, all the fluid which was originally in the lower part of the working cylinder cannot fit into the upper part because the piston rod has filled some of the void. This fluid is forced down through the lower compression valve into the reservoir area.

The amount of compression (jounce) control is dictated by the amount of force needed to transfer hydraulic fluid from the working cylinder into the reservoir.

Do you need new shocks?

Shock absorbers deteriorate gradually, especially shocks originally installed by the automobile's manufacturer and replacement units that are warranted for a specific period rather than "life." Deterioration is deceptive. It doesn't happen suddenly. Drivers become accustomed to the gradual changes in driving "feel" that take place. You never really know how much you need shocks until after you've replaced them. Suddenly your car will be riding like it was new again.

However, being aware of trouble signs will allow you to spot worn shocks before they cause too many problems. Problems include loss of stability, driver control and braking efficiency; decreased tire life; premature damage to springs, suspension and steering-linkage components; and a decrease in your riding comfort.

Trouble signs

The following are signs which indicate that your car may need new shocks:
● Shocks that have seen 20,000 to 25,000 miles if they are original equipment, or replacement units that have exceeded the mileage warranty set by the manufacturer.
● Oil on a shock's barrel, which signifies seal deterioration.
● Worn bushings. Test by trying to shake the shock. A shock that shakes is one that either has loose mountings or bushings that are worn.
● Physical damage. A broken rod that you can see by lifting the car, so shocks are extended, is physical damage. Also, large dents in the case.
● Scuffed or badly spot-worn tires.
● The car bottoms out when negotiating harsh bumps or when coming to a sudden stop.
● The car is hard to handle, swaying on turns, bouncing on smooth roads, and/or lacking control on curves.
● Shocks that fail the push-and-bounce test. Push down hard at each corner of the car two or three times. Let go on the end of a downstroke. If the corner bounces more than 1½ cycles, the shock should be replaced.

Two important tips

1. If one shock needs to be replaced, the other shock on the same axle should be replaced. The other two can be left in service if they aren't damaged or worn.

2. Replacing shock absorbers won't cure riding and driving problems caused by other conditions. According to a maker of shocks, "Excessive bottoming due to weak or sagging springs can't be helped by new shock absorbers. Nor can they (shocks) correct shimmy caused by unbalanced tires, bad front-wheel bearings or worn front-end parts."

Picking a shock

Shock absorbers come in three general types: replacement, load-carrying or special purpose.
Replacement shocks look like original-equipment shocks. Some *are* comparable. Others have larger cylinder bores and pistons, greater-diameter piston rods and heavier valving. These heavier-duty units compensate for wear to the car's

suspension system, withstand more rigorous driving conditions, and/or support heavier loads.

Replacement shocks may be classified as OEM-comparable (original equipment), heavy-duty, extra-heavy-duty, adjustable or MacPherson. Here, in general, is the purpose of each:
● OEM-comparable shocks are similar to the vehicle's original equipment. They are designed for normal driving and light loads. Being the least expensive units available, they usually carry a specified rather than "lifetime" warranty.
● Heavy-duty shocks can provide longer life than OEM-comparable units. They normally have a "lifetime" warranty and cost more. They should be used on a car with suspension parts that have "set." Heavy-duty shocks allow the car to handle heavier loads and more high-speed driving.
● Extra-heavy-duty replacement shocks are designed for light trucks, recreational vehicles, station wagons and cars that pull lightweight trailers of the boat and camper types.
● Adjustable shock absorbers are offered by a few manufacturers. They allow you to set the shocks for various conditions, permitting regular, firm or extra-firm support.
● MacPherson replacement cartridges allow you to replace original equipment cartridges without discarding strut housings. MacPherson units are used on most imported cars.

Load-carrying shocks

Load-carrying shocks are front and rear units that have the shocks combined with coil springs. Air-adjustable shocks also fall into this classification. Front and rear load-carrying units help you maintain maximum vehicle control and prevent damage to the suspension when hauling house trailers.

Air-adjustable shocks

Air-adjustable shocks provide the *occasional* trailer-towing driver with flexibility. When towing your trailer, adding air to the shock provides maximum support. When the trailer isn't being towed, air should be bled from the shocks.

An air-adjustable unit is the same as a regular replacement shock absorber with the exception of the added air chamber. Owners of vans, recreational and off-road vehicles who vary the weight of the load they carry from one time to another will also find air-adjustable shocks useful.

Special-purpose shock absorbers include those for racing cars, medium and heavy trucks, and buses.

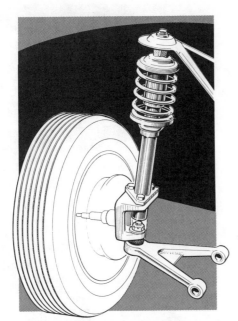

REPLACEMENT cartridges for Mac-Pherson-strut, front-suspension shocks make do-it-yourself work easy.

Replacing shocks

Don't buy shocks unless they are accompanied by instructions. In addition to the manufacturer's suggestions, here is a list of "dos" and "don'ts" you should keep in mind when replacing shocks.

● Just before you begin work, lay out all parts from the packages. Make sure the mounting components of each shock are present. Take each shock in hand, hold it vertically, and pump it up and down to work air out of the chambers.

● Make sure the car is firmly supported. You don't want it dropping on your head. If you are replacing rear shock absorbers of a car equipped with rear coil springs, don't let the rear wheels hang. The rear axle must be supported by a jack stand close to the shocks to keep springs in place when old shocks are removed, because shock absorber tension holds springs in position. Springs may also be supported by placing wedges between the suspension and axle.

Caution: If shocks are removed without the axle being supported, the axle can drop suddenly and may injure you and damage vehicle components.

● Don't twist studs off old shocks. You can dam-age the threads of the mounting seat, which is a part of the car. If nuts are rusted, give them a liberal dose of penetrating oil a day or two before you are going to do the job. Before applying oil, use a wire brush to remove rust and dirt from the mount threads.

● As you remove the mounting hardware, notice the order of position. Be sure to reassemble new mounting hardware in this order.

● Normally, to remove front shocks, hold the upper stem so it doesn't turn as you remove upper hardware. Then remove hardware holding the lower mounting and pull the shock out from the bottom.

Note: Lower hardware of front shocks is accessible from below. Upper hardware may not be. If not, get to it through the engine compartment. Hardware is either atop the fender housing or is reached by removing a rubber splash shield over the housing.

● Normally, to remove the rear shocks, disconnect upper, then lower hardware. If upper hardware is not visible, get to it via the trunk.

● In some cases of front shock installation, you may have to enlarge the hole in the lower suspension arm slightly to permit insertion of the shock's stem. Do this by tapping the inside edge of the hole, or by filing or grinding. Enlarge the hole just enough to accept the stem. You must never file or grind the shock as a perfectly smooth finish is required if the shock is to perform its function.

● When installing rear shocks, see that brake and fuel lines and exhaust pipes clear the units. Clearance should be checked with the car's body extended up and then pushed down after shocks have been installed—that is, with the wheels hanging and then by pressing down on the corners of the car. If necessary, move lines and pipes to obtain clearance.

● Never grip the piston rod of a new shock with any tool. Just a small nick or scratch in the rod can cut the seal. This will allow fluid to leak out and the shock will be useless.

● When installing shocks having stud-type mountings, don't overtighten the nut. The rubber bushing should be squeezed only enough to give it the same diameter as the retaining washers. Keep your touch delicate.

● Replacing air-adjustable shocks is similar to replacing standard shocks. However, there are additional steps to observe. For one, you have to disconnect air connections. Make sure you know these steps. They are listed in the instructions that come with the shocks.

Swimming pool shape-up

■ WHEN WARM WEATHER is on its way, the time is right to tune up your swimming pool so you can enjoy it during those hot summer days. Opening your pool properly can be easier, and taking care of your pool all season can be less demanding, if you follow the steps suggested here.

The basic strategy is to get your pool to the point where you can follow a simple, regular maintenance schedule. The steps required to open your pool will take two to four days to complete, depending on how well you protected your pool during the winter and how large it is. The steps to keep your pool clean should be followed all season.

Fill the pool

If you've properly winterized your pool, cleanup should be a minimal task. The recommended level for filling most pools is to the middle of the skimmer, the built-in device that traps surface debris.

Pool water evaporates and is dragged and splashed out by swimmers. You'll have to add water periodically to maintain proper level.

Check equipment

Check the pump, filter and circulating system. Refer to the owner's manual for installing parts removed for winter storage. Make sure mechanical components are clean and in proper working order.

To reinstall the pump/motor, first turn off the power at the control panel. Replace the gasket between the pump's tank and seal plate if it is damaged. Reinstall the drain plugs. Check the pump shaft for free movement. With power on, prime the pump following instructions in the owner's manual.

Determine pool capacity

Though pool water may appear clean and clear, if neglected it can quickly become a breeding place for microscopic bacteria and tiny plant life called *algae*. Bacteria, viruses and algae cannot multiply in pool water that's been properly treated with an inorganic chlorine sanitizer.

Before you can start the chemical treatment of your pool water, you must determine the pool's capacity in gallons to give correct dosages. If the pool is rectangular or square, multiply length x width x average depth (feet) x 7.5 to determine total gallons (7.5 represents the number of gallons in a cubic foot of water). If the pool is circular, multiply diameter x diameter x average depth x 5.9. If oval-shaped, multiply long diameter x short diameter x average depth x 5.9.

Adjust pH level

The pH level is a measure of the acidity or alkalinity of water. Unless the water in your pool is within a certain pH range indicated by a test kit, chlorine disinfectant won't be able to kill the bacteria.

The level at which chlorine optimally sanitizes ranges from 7.2 to 7.8. The pH scale runs from zero to 14. To get an accurate measure, follow the manufacturer's directions in your pool kit.

If pH is too *low,* chlorine dissipates rapidly, pipes and fittings can become corroded, plaster can become etched and swimmers can get an irritating eye burn.

If pH is too *high,* scale forms, pool water turns cloudy and swimmers get eye burn just as they do when pH is too low.

If your pool contains more than 1000 gallons of water, it's essential that you test the pH level of your water at least once a week. To get the pH level between 7.2 and 7.6 you should buy a reliable pool-test kit. The test kit uses a phenol red indicator solution that changes color at different pH levels. It should also have an OTD (orthotoluidine solution) test involving color changes for chlorine residual.

If the pH level is too low, add a pH-plus chemical; if the level is too high, add a pH-minus chemical.

Adjust total alkalinity

After you've adjusted the pH level, adjusting total alkalinity helps *keep* the pH in the proper range. The three main alkaline chemicals—carbonate, bicarbonate and hydroxide—dissolved in the water in the proper proportion act as a buffer to prevent pH change.

Use a kit to test for total alkalinity. Test it weekly and maintain it between 80 and 150 parts per million (ppm, the standard measure of concentration in swimming pools). Your pool-supply dealer can also tell you if an alkalinity problem exists in your area and can provide formulations needed to correct it.

Superchlorinate the water

Superchlorinating means applying 5 to 10 times the regular daily dose of chlorine to water. The two primary reasons for adding chlorine are: 1) to disinfect—kill water-borne organisms and algae; 2) to oxidate—burn out undesirable solids, colors and odors. While all pools must be superchlorinated from time to time, it is a must when opening your pool for the season.

Before you superchlorinate, determine the capacity of your pool in gallons; then determine the needed dosage of superchlorinator following directions on the package. Wait until the residual chlorine is at the recommended level of 1.0 to 1.5 ppm according to the test kit before stabilizing your pool water. You might want to superchlorinate at night and then test the water the following morning.

Superchlorination is an extra-heavy dose of chlorine—roughly 1 oz. of dry chlorine (65 or 70 percent available chlorine) added to 1000 gallons of water.

The chlorine residual should be kept between 0.6 and 1.0 ppm for unstabilized pools, and between 1.0 and 1.5 ppm for stabilized pools.

You should superchlorinate when opening a pool for the season, when refilling a pool after a long period of sunny and hot weather, heavy use, severe rain or windstorms, and whenever unpleasant tastes and odors are present in pool water. A shock treatment should be used if algae patches appear on pool walls or submerged fixtures, or if the water gives off an objectionable odor.

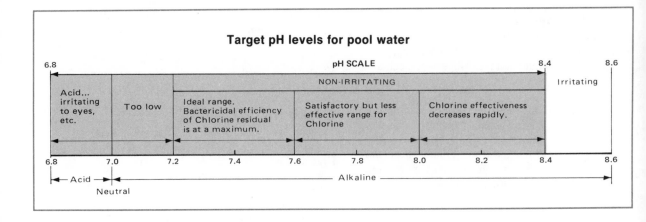

Target pH levels for pool water

Shock treatment is twice as powerful as superchlorination—1 oz. of dry chlorine (65 or 70 percent available chlorine) added to 500 gallons of water.

There are several types of chlorinating products on the market. Among them are liquid chlorine and calcium hypochlorite, which tend to lose effectiveness after a few hours due to the action of sunlight. On the other hand, chlorine concentrate in tablets or granular form contain a built-in stabilizer that resists sunlight-induced chlorine decay.

Handle dry chlorine with care

Never mix calcium hypochlorite with anything but water. It should not be mixed or contaminated with any foreign substances, including household products, soap or paint products, solvents, acids, pool chemicals, vinegar, garbage, beverages, oils, pine oil or dirty rags. Always keep burning material such as a lit cigarette away from any container of dry chlorine.

Stabilize the water

Since the sun's ultraviolet energy tends to dissipate available chlorine in pool water, pool owners who live in areas experiencing long periods of sunshine and heat may find that the chlorine residual in their pool water is being quickly consumed.

This problem can be overcome by stabilizing pool water with a chemical called *cyanuric acid*. Cyanuric acid protects the chlorine residual in pool water, yet it is nontoxic, does not affect the disinfection process and does not decompose.

Watch out for chlorine lock

If you decide to stabilize your pool water, even though you may have followed the manufac-

turer's directions to the letter, an excessive amount of cyanuric acid in the water can reduce the effectiveness of your chlorine sanitizer.

To remedy this condition, use a test kit that checks levels of cyanuric acid. If the level is too high, remove enough water from the pool so that the 25 to 50 ppm stabilizer level is achieved when the pool is refilled.

Keep your filter clean

The two most commonly used filters are sand filters and diatomaceous-earth filters. Pool water is recirculated through the filter under pressure created by a pump. Increased pressure is usually an indication of ineffective filtration.

A pressure buildup across the filter occurs when the filter is clogged with sediment and dirt from the pool. The best cure is to backwash it (reverse the flow of water) according to the manufacturer's instructions.

Use vacuuming equipment

Swimming-pool vacuum cleaners operate on the same principle as ordinary home vacuum cleaners except that water is drawn through the machine instead of air. Sediment and dirt drawn from the pool floor and sides are carried through the cleaner's piping for removal through its filter.

Don't forget the skimmer

Practically all pools have an automatic surface skimmer built directly into the pool or attached to the filtering system to remove leaves, bugs and other floating objects from the water. During filtration, surface water is drawn through the skimmer and into the filter, carrying off dust, oil film and other inert matter before it can settle to the pool floor.

Computerized analysis

To make pool maintenance somewhat easier, computer systems that can identify potential problems in the pool water are available. The water can be tested before the pool is filled, after it is filled or during the season.

Basically, a water sample is run through tests to analyze and balance it. The results, along with information about the specific pool, are entered into a computer that completes a data sheet tell-ing *what* chemicals are needed and in what *order* and *quantity* they should be applied in order to maintain your pool water safely.

This service is available at pool dealers. It doesn't take the place of careful monitoring by pool owners, however. Before you purchase a large amount of chemicals based on the results of such a test, it pays to satisfy yourself that the chemicals are actually needed.

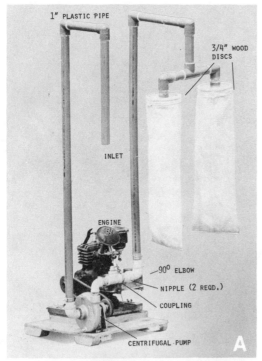

1" PLASTIC PIPE

3/4" WOOD DISCS

INLET

ENGINE

90° ELBOW

NIPPLE (2 REQD.)

COUPLING

CENTRIFUGAL PUMP

A

B

Swimming pool filter you can make

■ YOU CAN RIG A FILTER for your 15-ft. aboveground pool from an old lawn-mower engine, a 30-gpm centrifugal pump, some 1-in. plastic pipe and two canvas bags.

To use the filter, you first prime the pump by running a garden hose in the intake pipe. Next you place diatomaceous earth in a bucket and mix with water until you have a thick slurry. (Use ½ lb. of earth for each filter bag.) Submerge the bucket in the pool under the intake pipe (photo D), and with the pump running, suck the slurry into the canvas bags. The earth, coating sides of the bags, does the filtering. It takes about six hours a day to filter a 15-ft. pool.

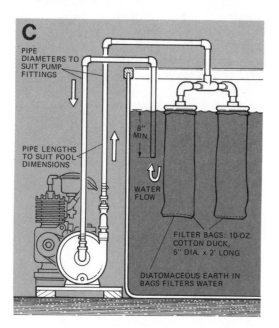

C

PIPE DIAMETERS TO SUIT PUMP FITTINGS

PIPE LENGTHS TO SUIT POOL DIMENSIONS

8" MIN.

WATER FLOW

FILTER BAGS: 10-OZ. COTTON DUCK, 5" DIA. x 2' LONG

DIATOMACEOUS EARTH IN BAGS FILTERS WATER

THE WOOD DISCS that hold the filter bags (photo B), are cut from ¾-in. solid wood, grooved around the edge for drawstrings, waterproofed with three coats of marine paint and cemented to the plastic pipe with epoxy. Use two bags for 15-ft. pool, three for 18-ft. Intake pipe should extend at least 8 in. in water to prevent pump cavitation (diagram C) and permit swimming while filter runs. Each supply pipe should be about 20 in. long. If near an outlet, electric motor can be used to drive the pump; use a gas engine if your pool is too far from the house.

D

Cabana for your pool

■ THERE ARE two distinct advantages to be gained from erecting a small structure adjacent to your pool. For one thing, you'll keep wet bathers from dripping water throughout the house because they'll have a convenient place to dry off and change. And when the pool is closed down at the end of the season, the little house can be put to good use for winter storage of seasonal items such as tractors, lawn furniture and the like.

This handsome cabana gives 84 sq. ft. (it measures approximately 7 x 12 ft.) for year-round use to suit your family's needs. Construction is conventional as can be seen in the drawings. Experience has proven that it is far more convenient if it is located close to the pool. If the apron around your pool is too narrow to accommodate the house, it is well worth the slight extra effort and

investment to increase the apron on one end, or, if you would rather have the house located elsewhere, simply add a connecting flagstone walk between the new slab and the existing apron next to the pool.

The house is built following standard building procedures. First, stake out the desired location

CABANA PROVIDES SPACE for bathers changing to swim togs and, as a bonus, there is extra storage for all of your lawn equipment and a tractor rider-mower.

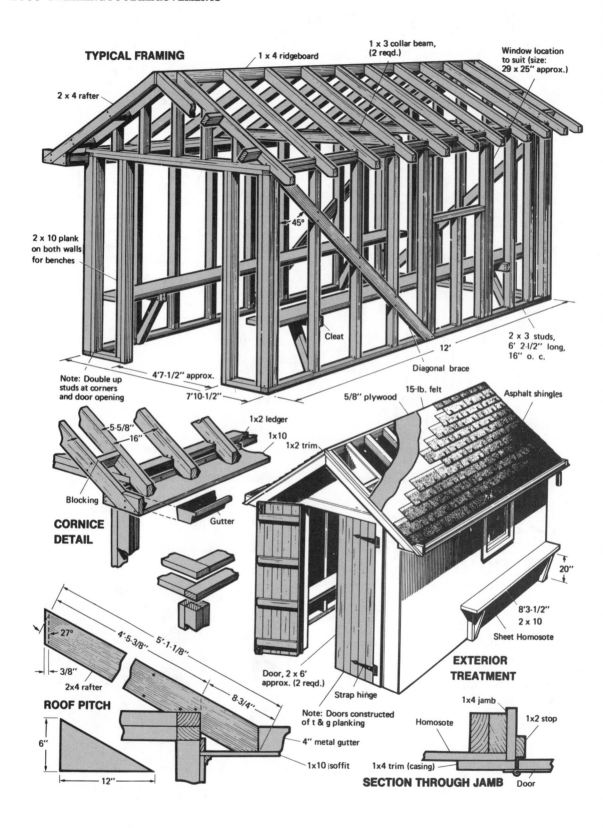

TYPICAL FRAMING

1 x 4 ridgeboard

1 x 3 collar beam, (2 reqd.)

Window location to suit (size: 29 x 25" approx.)

2 x 4 rafter

45°

2 x 10 plank on both walls for benches

Cleat

2 x 3 studs, 6' 2-1/2" long, 16" o. c.

12'

Diagonal brace

4'7-1/2" approx.

7'10-1/2"

Note: Double up studs at corners and door opening

5/8" plywood

15-lb. felt

Asphalt shingles

5-5/8"

16"

1x2 ledger

1x10

1x2 trim

Blocking

Gutter

CORNICE DETAIL

20"

8'3-1/2"
2 x 10

Sheet Homosote

27°

4'-5-3/8"

5'-1-1/8"

3/8"

2x4 rafter

8-3/4"

ROOF PITCH

6"

12"

Door, 2 x 6' approx. (2 reqd.)

Strap hinge

Note: Doors constructed of t & g planking

4" metal gutter

1x10 soffit

EXTERIOR TREATMENT

1x4 jamb

1x2 stop

Homosote

1x4 trim (casing)

SECTION THROUGH JAMB

Door

2-FT.-WIDE DOORS open up to make way for a riding tractor. If you don't have a tractor, a single door will do.

and remove all topsoil. Dig and pour footings around the perimeter to meet local area requirements and then pour a 4 to 5-in.-thick slab. (Before starting actual construction, check with your local building department; you may be required to obtain a building permit.) If the existing pool slab is wide enough to accommodate the little house, simply lay a double bead of caulking on the concrete over which the sole plates are laid. Use screws and lead anchors to secure them.

The 2x3s used for the studding provide more than adequate strength because there is a rather steep roof pitch to eliminate snow (load) accumulation during the winter months. The rafters are nominal 2x4s nailed 16 in. o.c., each directly over a stud. For ventilation, install a windows might be on sale at the local lumberyard. The rafters are covered with ⅝-in. plywood, followed by 15-lb. felt and asphalt shingles. Wall construction was kept simple (and economical) by using 4x8-ft. sheets of Homosote, which stands up well against the weather. It can be painted at first, and, as funds are available, covered with siding or shingles to match your home.

If desired, the cabana can be partitioned inside to provide individual dressing rooms. Or you can leave it as one big room so that winter storage is not cut down or made impractical.

Install a standard 2½ to 3-ft.-wide single door in the conventional manner. A wider doorway can accommodate a riding tractor if you have one.

You can leave the interior unfinished. For convenience, however, install two 2x10-in. benches the full length of both walls. The diagonal bracing provides more than adequate strength and there should be no noticeable sagging. Because the house is next to the pool, a short bench was fastened along an outside wall. Thus, whenever youngsters have a gang in, there is more than enough seating for everybody.

DOORS ARE held closed by a pair of sliding bolts on one, and a latch and pull combination on the other.

Picturesque poolhouse

■ IT DOESN'T TAKE LONG after the christening of a new pool to realize that you need a pool-side cabana to save wear and tear on the main house. You can use simplified construction techniques, and inexpensive materials. Prudent shopping, of course, keeps total cost down. Though small, this house performs five functions: In addition to housing the pool filter and accessories, it offers a screened-in area for bugfree barbecues, a lavatory and dressing room, a deck for sunbathing and a playhouse for youngsters.

The building rests on a 4-in. concrete slab poured on a perimeter footing. For framing use 2x3s for studs and 2x4s for joists. The cedar shingles on the A-roof and gable ends are No. 4 and the exterior siding is V-grooved ⅜-in. exterior plywood.

You can use fin-type windows. They are extremely easy to install and, once in place, are practically maintenance-free.

Since indoor-outdoor carpeting is used on the sundeck, absolute waterproofing is a must. To do it, cover the ½-in.-plywood sheathing with two layers of overlapped 15-pound felt. Next, to protect the carpet from stains, put down a cover of 6-mil. polypropylene plastic. Notice that the deck is slightly pitched to provide positive drainage. Rainwater passing through the carpeting is carried over the plastic to the edge of the building for runoff.

YOUNGSTERS CAN'T resist second-level play house, use it frequently for overnight sleep outs.

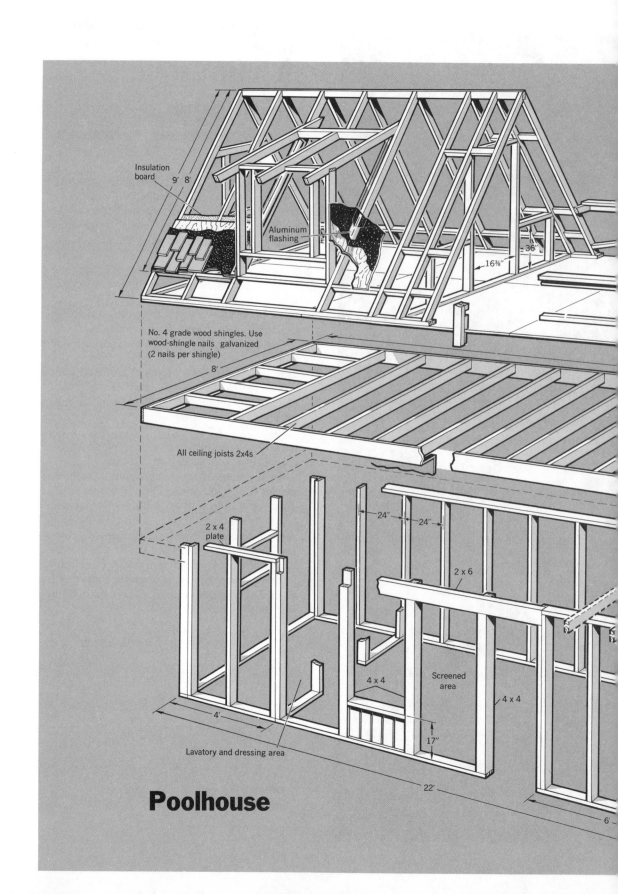

Insulation board

9' 8'

Aluminum flashing

36"

16⅜"

No. 4 grade wood shingles. Use wood-shingle nails galvanized (2 nails per shingle)

8'

All ceiling joists 2x4s

2 x 4 plate

24"   24"

2 x 6

4 x 4

Screened area

4 x 4

17"

4'

Lavatory and dressing area

22'

6

Poolhouse

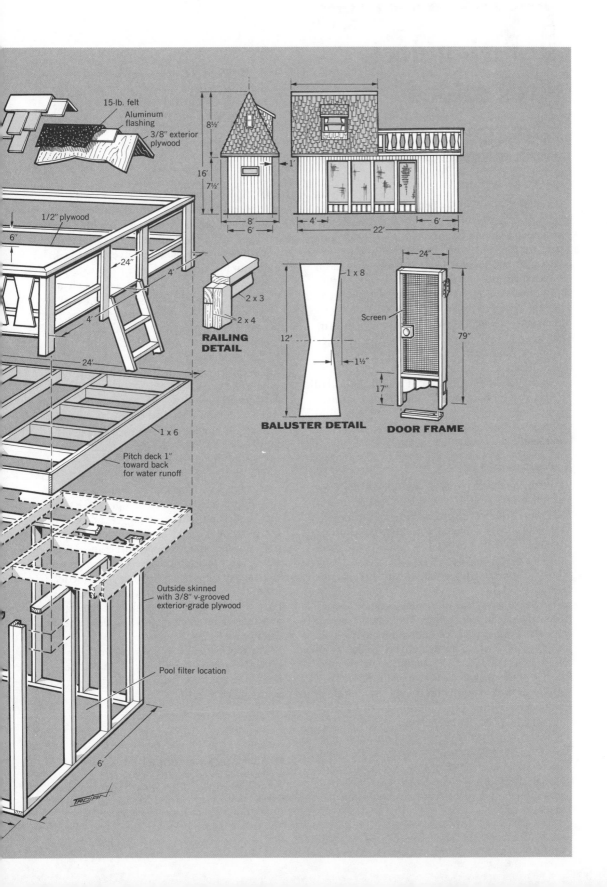

15-lb. felt
Aluminum flashing
3/8" exterior plywood

1/2" plywood

6"

24'

4'

4'

RAILING DETAIL

2 x 3

2 x 4

8½'

16'

7½'

1

8'

6'

4'

22'

6'

24'

Screen

24"

79"

17"

DOOR FRAME

1 x 8

12'

1½'

BALUSTER DETAIL

24'

1 x 6

Pitch deck 1" toward back for water runoff

Outside skinned with 3/8" v-grooved exterior-grade plywood

Pool filter location

6'

Diving deck gives added storage

■ ABOVE-GROUND POOLS have become very popular. A common problem, however, is providing a diving arrangement as a "launching pad" for the youngsters. In addition to being unsafe, a diving board is just too hard to rig in an elevated position.

We were determined to solve this problem, and the diving deck shown here is the result. Our main goal was to provide a safe diving platform. But, in addition, since footage would be taken from the yard, we wanted the space beneath the deck to serve as seasonal storage as well as to house the pool filter system. It was also decided to place the stairs behind the door to protect young ones. Extras that "make" the structure include a foot bath, indoor/outdoor carpeting and nautical rope for the railing.

Construction is easy

Design is basic; there are no fancy, frilly construction techniques. Tried construction methods were used to insure maximum sturdiness, yet details were kept simple to keep costs down to a minimum. For example, careful layout permitted cutting the deck from just two 4x8-ft. sheets of exterior plywood with practically no waste.

Overall dimensions of the deck can be varied to suit the size of your family. The version shown provides ample room for sunbathing as well as diving. One critical measurement to keep in mind—when laying out your structure—is the portion of the deck that overhangs the pool. This can be altered to suit without any problems.

The four-by-four posts are anchored to footings which should be below your area frostline. Once the four-bys are in place, and the concrete has set, the post-holes can be backfilled and cutoff marks at the top located. To do this, determine desired height on one corner post and mark off the other posts using a mason's line and line-level.

Top and bottom rails are simply spiked to the posts and framing is completed with joists and bridging installed. The rails and posts are fitted with cleats positioned to give a setback (architectural shadowline) when the exterior plywood panels are in place. (In place of cleats, the 2x4 rails can be edge-rabbeted on a table saw.)

Doors to the storage area and stairs are simply plywood panels framed with rails and stiles fastened to the structure with strap hinges. Catches to hold them closed and vertical half-round moldings complete their construction.

The stairs

A limited run made a steep riser-to-tread ratio a must. But, unlike conventional stairs, it is not a drawback. Actually, their "marine-ladder" steepness adds to the nautical design.

The deck can be finished using an exterior latex paint with some fine masonry sand mixed in for skidproofing. (Or, you can purchase a ready-mix sand paint.) But our suggestion is to cover the plywood with 15-lb. felt, followed by 6-mil polyethylene and outdoor carpeting. (The felt waterproofs the storage area while the polyethylene prevents any possible stains from the felt rising to the carpet.) Either way the finished surface is an effective safeguard against accidental skids and falls. The latter method is just more comfortable underfoot.

The foot bath at bottom is optional (it's an inexpensive plastic baby bathtub), but it does decrease the mud tracked up to the deck carpet by overzealous youngsters.

AN ABOVE-GROUND POOL mandates a structure alongside for diving fun. This one has steps inside that are inaccessible when the door is locked. Space behind the doors is ample for year-round storage of bike and yard equipment plus the pool filter.

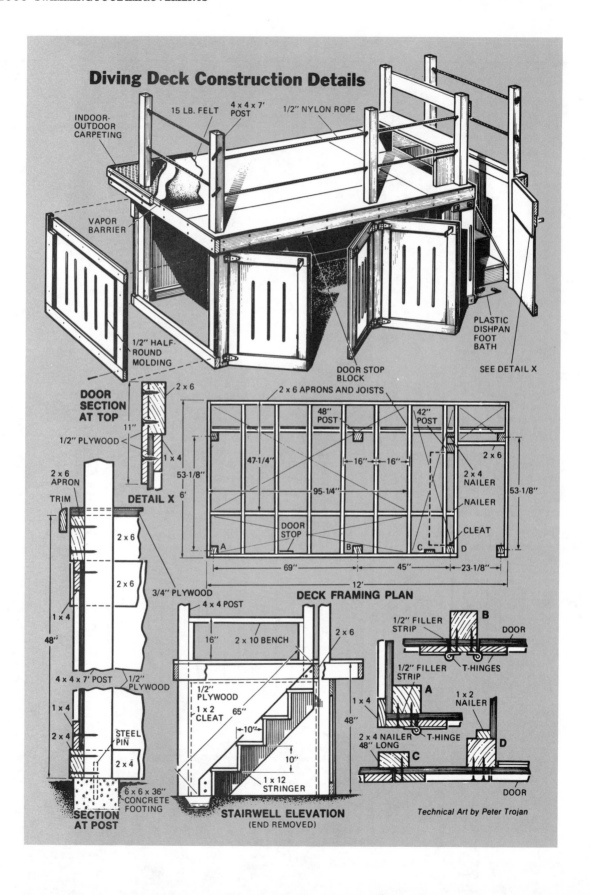

Diving Deck Construction Details

15 LB. FELT
4 x 4 x 7' POST
1/2" NYLON ROPE
INDOOR-OUTDOOR CARPETING
VAPOR BARRIER
1/2" HALF-ROUND MOLDING
DOOR STOP BLOCK
PLASTIC DISHPAN FOOT BATH
SEE DETAIL X

DOOR SECTION AT TOP
2 x 6
11"
1/2" PLYWOOD
1 x 4
DETAIL X

2 x 6 APRONS AND JOISTS
48" POST
42" POST
47-1/4"
16" 16"
95-1/4"
2 x 6
2 x 4 NAILER
NAILER
CLEAT
DOOR STOP
A B C D
53-1/8"
6'
53-1/8"
69" 45" 23-1/8"
12'

DECK FRAMING PLAN

2 x 6 APRON
TRIM
2 x 6
2 x 6
3/4" PLYWOOD
1 x 4
48"
4 x 4 x 7' POST
1/2" PLYWOOD
1 x 4
2 x 4
STEEL PIN
2 x 4
6 x 6 x 36" CONCRETE FOOTING

SECTION AT POST

4 x 4 POST
2 x 10 BENCH
16"
2 x 6
1/2" PLYWOOD
1 x 2 CLEAT
65"
10"
10"
1 x 12 STRINGER

STAIRWELL ELEVATION
(END REMOVED)

1/2" FILLER STRIP
B
DOOR
T-HINGES
1/2" FILLER STRIP
A
1 x 2 NAILER
1 x 4
48"
2 x 4 NAILER 48" LONG
T-HINGE
C
D
DOOR

Technical Art by Peter Trojan

INDOOR-OUTDOOR carpeting insures skidproof footing. It is laid over 15-lb. felt and 6-mil polyethylene.

THE PLATFORM overhangs the pool slightly. Measurements might vary from the drawing to suit your pool.

Since a slab wasn't used here, you'll notice in the photos that the structure walls leave space at the bottom to permit rainwater runoff. If you prefer slab construction, you are well advised to install a block wall or form the slab to create a curb. A standard soleplate can then be installed, with posts toenailed to the plates, and conventional wall framing used. But remember that a slab would require the addition of a pitched apron in front of the doors to provide positive water runoff. The apron will also make it easier to roll bikes and other wheeled vehicles in and out of the storage area.

To finish, the entire structure was primed and painted (inside and out) with a high-quality, latex house paint. (For additional safety, the stair treads could also be carpeted or coated with a sandmix paint to make them skidproof.)

The prototype project shown took the owner four weekends to complete. He started it late in April, and by the time the thermometer climbed to swimming temperatures he was happily spending his vacation atop his "Slip-Proof Diving Deck" in his own back yard.

THE STORAGE DOORS are built with one-by stock and ¼-in. plywood. Half-round moldings are added to give a decorative touch. As shown at right, the prebuilt stairs are lowered into position after frame is complete.

Back-yard resort from your above-ground pool

■ YOUR ABOVE-GROUND pool will nestle beautifully into this enchanting back-yard entertainment center. It makes your yard into an outdoor living resort but the pool still remains the focal point.

The decks and privacy walls were designed to take full advantage of the beauty of such common woods as western pine and fir. When this wood is left natural (and treated for extra protection with a clear preservative), it will eventually weather to a subtle silver gray. This soft and pleasing tone works to achieve an even greater harmony with its surroundings.

Where to start

Using stakes and mason's line, carefully lay out the entire deck to suit your property and pool size. Before you go any farther it would be a good idea to make a visit to your local building authority. Make certain that your intended structure conforms to local building codes before you begin turning the first spadeful of earth. Start by staking out what will be the upper level to suit your particular pool and needs. Next, work up a scale drawing of deck elevations—and an elevation for a fence around the upper deck. The fence should be no less than 1 ft. above the upper deck and no more than 3 ft. higher than the flooring.

Elevations for both levels as well as the fence are determined by several factors, including pool height, land contour and existing plantings. All three elements should be taken into careful account before you begin.

Securing deck to footings

The lower deck rests on cylindrical footings. These are made by pouring concrete into stan-dard Sonotube forms. The deck joists, in turn, are secured to footings using commercially available hardware. Another technique is to use drift pins embedded in the concrete. Decking is nailed to the joists with 8d hot-dipped galvanized nails. Be sure to leave a uniform space between the 2x6 planks to allow rain to drain off and for swelling and shrinking of the wood.

The near side of the upper level is built directly over the edge of the lower level. For that reason, the joist along that edge of the lower level is dou-bled up to create a beam. The pool side of the upper level is supported by three 4x4 posts se-cured atop cylindrical footings with drift pins.

Metal joist hangers are used throughout the entire project. They are readily available at lum-beryards and homebuilding centers. Use of such hardware makes the task a lot easier, yet assures excellent structural stability. If you frame around any existing plantings, as we did with the tree at stage center, you will inevitably have to cut at least one joist and install headers. And don't for-get to take into consideration that a tree such as this will grow larger through the years.

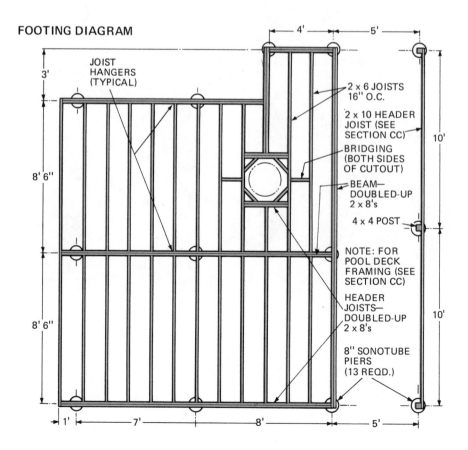

FOOTING DIAGRAM

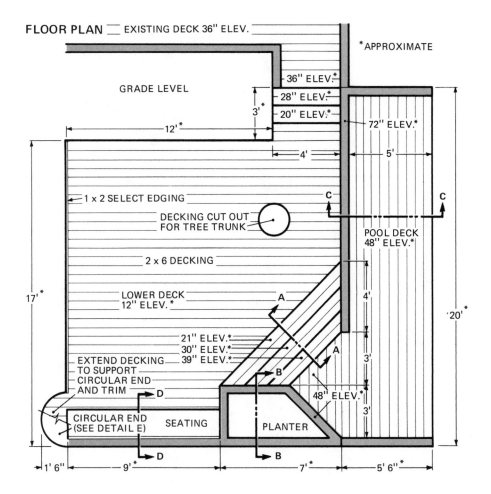

FLOOR PLAN — EXISTING DECK 36" ELEV.

*APPROXIMATE

GRADE LEVEL

36" ELEV.*
28" ELEV.*
20" ELEV.*
72" ELEV.*

3'*

12'*

4'

5'

1 x 2 SELECT EDGING

C   C

DECKING CUT OUT
FOR TREE TRUNK

POOL DECK
48" ELEV.*

2 x 6 DECKING

17'*

LOWER DECK
12" ELEV.*

A

4'

'20'*

21" ELEV.*
30" ELEV.*
39" ELEV.*

A

EXTEND DECKING
TO SUPPORT
CIRCULAR END
AND TRIM

B

3'

D

48" ELEV.*

CIRCULAR END
(SEE DETAIL E)   SEATING   PLANTER

3'

1' 6"   9'*   D   B   7'*   5' 6"*

To minimize deflection (bounciness) in that area, you would be wise to install bridging between pairs of joists flanking both sides of the framed opening (see drawing). To create the round opening, simply install decking over the joists in a conventional manner, but leave a goodly amount to overhang the opening and cut the decking with a sabre saw.

The high point of this deck design is the privacy screen. This is established by installing the built-in seating planter wall. This line continues the line of the upper deck with the installation of the fence.

Note that the half-cylinder at the right end of the seat is supported by being cantilevered on extended decking in the corner, and by being tied into the wall behind the seat. Since the half-cylinder doesn't weigh very much, this procedure is structurally sound.

When building the steps to the upper deck, lay them out so that the riser height falls in the comfortable-to-navigate 6- to-7½-in. range.

Construction hints

● Make certain that all lumber that comes in close contact with the ground is thoroughly protected by wood preservative. Though joists rest on concrete piers, you are well advised to coat them immediately after they are installed. An alternative to this might be to purchase wood that has been pretreated at the mill to be "all-weather" stock.

● To prevent water problems or rot, the planter is fitted with a sheet-metal liner. To guarantee against water seepage, solder the corners with the box securely in place. Note that the liner folds over the planter sides and is capped by the top trim detail on the planter.

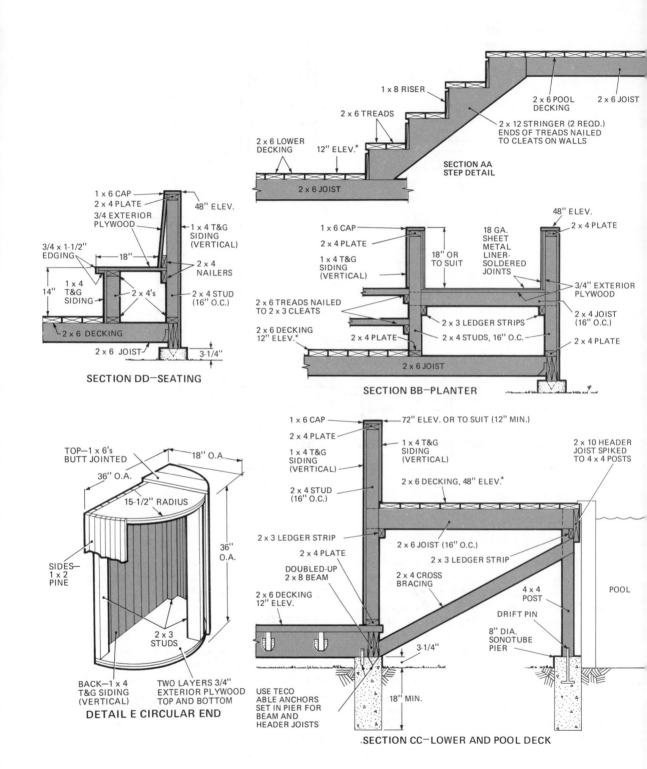

1 x 8 RISER

2 x 6 TREADS

2 x 6 LOWER DECKING

12" ELEV.*

2 x 6 JOIST

2 x 6 POOL DECKING

2 x 6 JOIST

2 x 12 STRINGER (2 REQD.) ENDS OF TREADS NAILED TO CLEATS ON WALLS

SECTION AA STEP DETAIL

1 x 6 CAP
2 x 4 PLATE
3/4 EXTERIOR PLYWOOD

48" ELEV.

1 x 4 T&G SIDING (VERTICAL)

3/4 x 1-1/2" EDGING

18"

2 x 4 NAILERS

1 x 4 T&G SIDING

14"

2 x 4's

2 x 4 STUD (16" O.C.)

2 x 6 DECKING

2 x 6 JOIST

3-1/4"

SECTION DD—SEATING

1 x 6 CAP
2 x 4 PLATE
1 x 4 T&G SIDING (VERTICAL)

48" ELEV.

2 x 4 PLATE

18" OR TO SUIT

18 GA. SHEET METAL LINER-SOLDERED JOINTS

3/4" EXTERIOR PLYWOOD

2 x 6 TREADS NAILED TO 2 x 3 CLEATS

2 x 3 LEDGER STRIPS

2 x 4 JOIST (16" O.C.)

2 x 6 DECKING 12" ELEV.*

2 x 4 PLATE

2 x 4 STUDS, 16" O.C.

2 x 4 PLATE

2 x 6 JOIST

SECTION BB—PLANTER

TOP—1 x 6's BUTT JOINTED

18" O.A.

36" O.A.

15-1/2" RADIUS

36" O.A.

SIDES— 1 x 2 PINE

2 x 3 STUDS

BACK—1 x 4 T&G SIDING (VERTICAL)

TWO LAYERS 3/4" EXTERIOR PLYWOOD TOP AND BOTTOM

DETAIL E CIRCULAR END

1 x 6 CAP
2 x 4 PLATE
1 x 4 T&G SIDING (VERTICAL)
2 x 4 STUD (16" O.C.)

72" ELEV. OR TO SUIT (12" MIN.)

1 x 4 T&G SIDING (VERTICAL)

2 x 6 DECKING, 48" ELEV.*

2 x 10 HEADER JOIST SPIKED TO 4 x 4 POSTS

2 x 3 LEDGER STRIP

2 x 4 PLATE

DOUBLED-UP 2 x 8 BEAM

2 x 6 DECKING 12" ELEV.

2 x 6 JOIST (16" O.C.)

2 x 3 LEDGER STRIP

2 x 4 CROSS BRACING

4 x 4 POST

POOL

DRIFT PIN

8" DIA. SONOTUBE PIER

3-1/4"

USE TECO ABLE ANCHORS SET IN PIER FOR BEAM AND HEADER JOISTS

18" MIN.

SECTION CC—LOWER AND POOL DECK

Vacation all summer in a low-cost pool

■ INVEST A FEW DAYS this summer and bring a piece of the ocean into your back yard. Above-ground pools are dotting lawns all across the country, and with good reason. Most are small enough to bring home in a station wagon, and big enough to keep your family and friends wet, happy and cool all summer long. Pool designs are pretty much the same, either round or oval, although different manufacturers offer a variety of finishes and assembly hardware. After you've shopped around, you should base your choice on two factors—quality and safety. Here are some guidelines:

Select from reputable makers. They will offer guarantees on filter tanks and warranties on pool liners. Stay away from pools with electro-galvanized steel walls. They look all right, but they're not durable. For a good-quality, economical pool, look for roll-formed aluminum or hot-dipped, galvanized steel walls. Extruded aluminum or steel walls with a copper additive are excellent quality but more expensive. Finishing should include a two or three-coat paint process with a final bonderizer application. A simple guide to quality is that aluminum pools should be embossed for strength and painted to resist corrosion. Steel pools should have corrugated walls, not flat sheeting. If you can't get this kind of information from a salesman, watch out.

The major responsibility for running a safe pool rests with the owner who must supervise who goes in and how they act. But there are areas you can't control and here's where a good manufacturer should step in to help. Most pool ladders can be easily climbed by children who can't swim once they get to the other side. When you're not around, this is a danger. To prevent it, safety ladders were developed. The outside steps and frame are hinge-mounted so they can

be swung up off the ground out of reach. This is good protection against a child's wandering over to take a dip when no adults are around.

Safety ladders will also help prevent accidents as swimmers get in and out of the pool because they are anchored, usually by two chains, to the edge of the pool wall. Most of them bear a sign saying NO DIVING, a caution that goes for the rim of the pool, too. A ladder without chains is likely to tip with the weight of a swimmer pulling up onto the step.

When electricity and water come together, accidents happen. You must decide how to run the electric cord to the pool (don't run the lawnmower over it), but the manufacturer should provide built-in protection against shock haz-

Putting in your pool

1. Pick the right site. Stay away from overhead obstructions, especially electrical lines. A level site with good drainage is best

2. Drive a stake in at the center of your site. Use string to scribe a circle two feet larger than your pool size. Note: avoid areas where chemical weed killers have been used

3. Check for level thoroughly. Use a level on top of a straight 2x4 to increase accuracy. Water in the pool will be level no matter what you do. But if the rim turns out to be uneven, you'll be wasting space at one end of the pool that could have been filled

4. Use temporary stakes between the support pads to keep the bottom rim in line as you work. Follow the manufacturer's instructions carefully—you're building the foundation for a large and heavy amount of water

5. Get some help for this step. The one-piece steel wall can be as wriggly as an eel. Use 1x2 stakes to keep the wall steady while you're fitting the rim

6. Get a good, tight assembly on your uprights. They're the backbone that keeps the wall rigid

7. Take off your shoes—they'll wreck the liner. Try for no wrinkles (you'll get a few anyway) and leave an overlap (check the specs for how much) at the top edge of the pool wall

8. Make sure you've built up a round cove of earth at the inside bottom edge of the pool wall. If you don't, the tremendous water pressure may force the liner under the wall and tear it

9. Installing the rim locks up a job well done

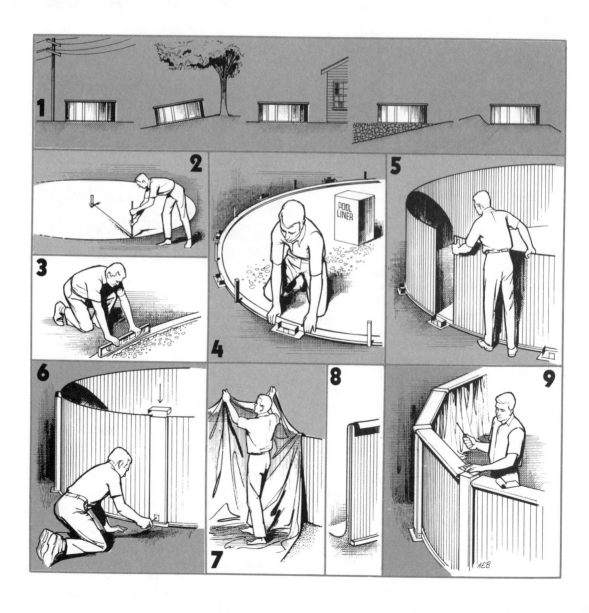

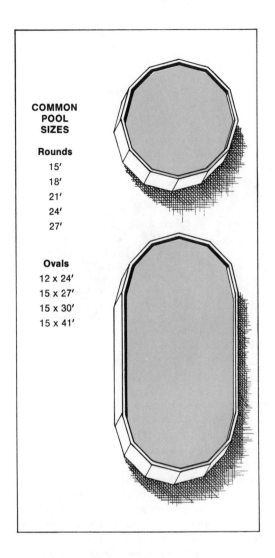

COMMON POOL SIZES

Rounds
15'
18'
21'
24'
27'

Ovals
12 x 24'
15 x 27'
15 x 30'
15 x 41'

Tools of the trade

Tamper	Packing down fresh earth
Shovel	Removing the sod
Wrench	Bolting the frame
Hammer	Driving rim stakes
Screwdriver	Assembling the uprights
Level	Checking the grade
Tape measure	Laying out the site
Rake	Clearing the dirt floor
Masking tape	Protecting the liner rim
String	Scribing the circle
Clothespins	Holding liner as you go

15-foot pools can be set up in a day. For larger ones you'll need a few friends and a weekend. Select a site that's as flat as possible. Dig down to create a level surface if you have to. Freshly built-up earth will compress and settle, causing part of the rim to sink with it. Enlist as much help as possible when you're fitting the steel wall into the bottom rim. It's like trying to hold five slippery eels by the tail—as you grab one, another slides away. Try a few 1x2 temporary stakes to brace one section while you're fitting the opposite side.

Smooth as silk

Before you fit the liner, go over all of the ground with a fine-tooth rake. A small pebble or sharp twig can work its way through the liner and cause a leak. Any hard edge will be extremely uncomfortable underfoot. Fit the liner carefully and be sure to provide enough fill to create a soft corner where the liner meets the bottom edge of the pool wall. Bare feet are mandatory during this operation. Get the liner as wrinkle-free as possible and leave a healthy overlap on the rim. A 16-gauge material, standard on most pools, doesn't have much of a tolerance for stretching. Twenty-gauge liners are available and will adjust to a stress without ripping.

A solar pool cover panel can raise the water temperature 10 to 15 degrees when floated on the surface. It rolls up for easy storage.

Choose the right pool and invest in quality equipment. It will pay off in years of summer fun for your family.

ards. Most codes now require you to use a GFCI on the circuit. Another safeguard is to look for a UL-approved label. This means that Underwriters Laboratories has inspected the electrical system. Some dealers may show you a UL tag on the wire, but that's not enough. Make sure the filter pump is tagged as well.

Most makers provide clear and complete installation instructions. A typical job is shown here to let you know what's involved. Twelve or

TV and video

■ VIDEO DEVICES ARE NOW AS COM-
MONPLACE as any other object of American
culture, including books and bathtubs. In less
than a half-century, video has become a mam-
moth industry, a major art form and a superb
hobby.

Any new development in TV and video can be
classified and judged by how the innovation creates, displays, stores or transmits the video signal.
To gain a better perspective for judging these
new products and developments, let's first look at
how a TV picture is created.

HOW VIDEO IS CREATED

Scanning

Any video picture is made by sending a very
thin stream of electrons to sample light and dark
patterns of an image which is focused by a lens
on the face of the pickup (or camera) tube. The
electron beam is concentrated into a small dot
and starts at the top left-hand corner, moving
across the screen in a more-or-less horizontal
line. When the electron beam finishes the first
row, it is turned off and aimed again at the left
side of the picture to start another scan line below
the one it just completed. After 262 lines it is at
the bottom of the camera tube. Total elapsed
time to get there: 1/60 of a second. Somewhere in
the middle of line 263, it is turned off and
snapped back to the top of the tube to scan the
spaces between the lines it just did. In just 1/30 of
a second, the electron beam scans 525 lines down

the image area and sends a continuous stream of
voltage changes to its associated circuits.

The varying intensity of light in the image creates
resistance difference across a target plate. At about
200-400 regular intervals on each scanned line (the
number varies with the sophistication of the system),
the electron beam detects the location and intensity of
light on the plate and converts the voltage differences
to voltage differences. Light areas will produce a
higher voltage output than darker areas of the image.

Semiconductor pickups. Some cameras use
semiconductors instead of tubes to pick up and translate the image into the electrical pulses.

Solid-state pickups come in two varieties: the
charge coupled device (CCD) and metal-oxide-sil-
icon semiconductor (MOS).

CCD and MOS sensors are about 1½ in. long by 1 in. wide and ⅟₁₆ in. thick. Dead center on the chip's surface is the imaging optic, measuring ½ or ⅓ in. diagonally depending on the maker. Embedded within the optic are nearly 200,000 light-sensitive picture elements, arranged by rows in the same 3:4 height-to-width ratio as a TV screen.

The optic is the business end of a solid-state sensor. Light entering the camera lens passes through a color separation filter and strikes the optic. Each light-sensitive element builds up an electrical charge proportionate to the intensity of the light at that location in the image. The solid-state sensor needs no fast-scanning electron beam to read the sampled light patterns. Instead, the charge built up in each picture element is stored in the potential well of a capacitor. In the case of CCD pickups, a voltage applied to the potential wells send each stored picture element scampering from one capacitor or the next, in bucket-brigade fashion. From left to right across each row,

the image fragments migrate from the top to the bottom of the optic at the transmission rate of TV. With MOS imaging devices, quick pulsing registers shift horizontally and vertically across the picture-element grid, continuously sampling momentary changes in the strength of the stored charges and then pass this information along to other circuits.

Frequency response. Each of the dots sampled in either tube or solid-state pickups represents a separate voltage cycle. Each frame scanned by the electron beam is made up of hundreds of thousands of these sampled dots. With 300 dots sampled on each line of a tube pickup, and 525 horizontal lines per frame, there are 157,500 dots per frame. Each second, 30 of these frames are sent out each containing about 4,725,000 voltage cycles of information. Solid state devices can produce even more. Even the most sophisticated hi-fi stereo systems rarely produces more than 20,000 cycles (20kHz) of sound information in a second. The response fidelity of TV circuits must be much higher than for audio.

The voltage variations from either a tube or solid-state pickup are amplified and massaged with other signals (important to your receiver but never seen) and radiated into the atmosphere—or circuited through wires—as electromagnetic energy. In this way, television signals are not unlike the signals from a simple telephone call or radio broadcast except that video has a voracious appetite for bandwidth in the radio frequency spectrum.

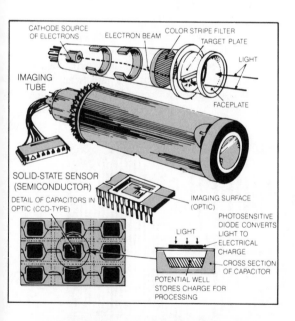

CATHODE SOURCE OF ELECTRONS

ELECTRON BEAM

COLOR STRIPE FILTER

TARGET PLATE

LIGHT

IMAGING TUBE

FACEPLATE

SOLID-STATE SENSOR (SEMICONDUCTOR)

DETAIL OF CAPACITORS IN OPTIC (CCD-TYPE)

IMAGING SURFACE (OPTIC)

PHOTOSENSITIVE DIODE CONVERTS LIGHT TO ELECTRICAL CHARGE

LIGHT

CROSS SECTION OF CAPACITOR

POTENTIAL WELL STORES CHARGE FOR PROCESSING

TUBE AND SOLID-STATE PICKUPS differ from each other in more than just size. The need for an electron beam to scan images accounts for the tube's bulk. Semiconductors send data directly from 200,000 light-sensitive picture elements. Chips are less susceptible to damage from shock and vibration, tolerating much more physical abuse than tubes. Semiconductors also do not have the tube's after-image lag, or streaking, comet-trail effect when the camera is passed across lights or bright images.

Bandwidth

Bandwidth has to do with the amount of the spectrum required to transmit the voltage patterns through a wire or into the air. It is measured in *Herzes:* cycles per second.

Video bandwidth is directly related to picture detail or *resolution*. Broadcast television in the U.S. and Canada (and many other places around the world) requires a video bandwidth of 4,200,000 cycles per second or 4.2 MegaHerz (MHz).

To gain perspective, contrast this requirement with telephone and radio. A telephone message uses only about 3000 Hz. A single TV channel is the equivalent of 1400 voice circuits! An AM radio network needs only 5000 Hz. A single TV channel could accommodate 840 different AM programs. An FM broadcast uses 15,000 Hz. A single TV frequency allocation could contain 280 of these high-fidelity transmissions.

The hunger for bandwidth makes video a voracious neighbor on the broadcast spectrum. That's one reason why we have so many fewer

TV stations than AM and FM radio stations. Economics is the other reason.

Color TV

Conventional color video is black-and-white times three. A system of color filters behind the camera lens separates the incoming image into the three primary colors of light: red-yellow, blue and green. Two additional types of signals are added to the array scanned by the picture tube: chroma and luminescence (hue and intensity of the colors).

HOW VIDEO IS DISPLAYED

CRT tubes

The display screen (technically known as a Cathode Ray Tube) is like the video pickup tube in reverse. The varying voltages of the stream of light-sampled dots cause the reproducing electron beam to project more or fewer electrons at tiny points lying in a fine grid pattern on the photo-sensitive surface of the picture tube. Points receiving higher voltages become brighter. Those receiving lower voltages remain darker.

The reason the electron beam scans only half the image area at one time has to do with flicker. If the beam scanned every line per frame—and there were only 30 frames per second—the video sequence would have a perceptible flicker in it. The interlaced scanning method results in 60 half-pictures per second. The persistence of vision in the human eye smooths these half-frames into a constant image, virtually free of any no-

THE DISPLAY OF IMAGES on your home receiver works on the same scanning principle as the camera pickup tube, only in reverse. Developments in digital receivers, such as the one shown here, are described in the article **TV's Third Generation.**

ticeable flicker. You've experienced this same persistence of vision if you've ever moved a flashlight back and forth rapidly. You know it is only a single spot of light, but you see the light pattern as a continuous line.

High-definition TV

In conventional TV pictures, your eyes do a marvelous job at guessing the shades and colors between the scanned lines. You mentally fill in the spaces between the lines and perceive the picture as one solid image. That's what your mind is conditioned to see and it works overtime to make you think the picture is, indeed, completely filled in.

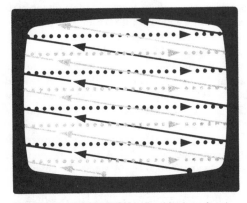

VERTICAL RESOLUTION is fixed by broadcast standards at 525 lines, with the electron beam scanning the face of the tube in two fields of 262½ lines each second. Electron gun begins at the top left-hand corner of screen, zigzags to complete first field, then races to top center to trace second field between lines of the first.

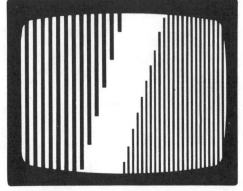

HORIZONTAL RESOLUTION varies with tube and circuit quality in the TV set. The number of individual dots sampled by the electron beam on each scanned line can be just a few (left side of screen) or many on better sets (right side of screen). Conventional television sets have about 250 lines of resolution; monitors have 330 to 400 lines.
More information about new high-resolution television receivers is in the article, **TV's Third Generation.**

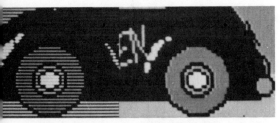

IN CONVENTIONAL TV PICTURES (left), your mind works overtime trying to fill in the information it knows should be between the scanned lines. In the new high-definition TV (right), a computer does most of that work for you, leaving a picture more than twice as sharp. An explanation of how that's done appears in the article that follows, **TV's Third Generation.**

Some TV receivers are now capable of high-definition TV (HDTV). In this system, a computer circuit in the receiver makes an educated guess about the color and intensity of the areas between each scanned line and then adds new lines to fill in the picture. The result is twice the number of scanned lines seen and more than twice the clarity and sharpness of the picture.

Color reception

To see video in color you must have a special color-receiving tube (along with all the supporting electronics). The conventional color display device is a three-in-one device. It has three different electron guns inside, each sending out the electronic signals for one of the three colors. The three guns converge their electron beams onto

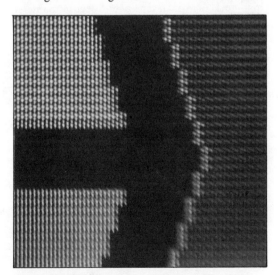

IN COLOR PICTURE TUBE, the electron beam aims at one of three color dots that are etched on the face of the tube. Because more space is needed for these color-dot triads, horizontal resolution and sharpness on a color set is much less than on a black-and-white.

one phosphorescent surface, each gun aiming only at dots of its own color.

(Some color TV sets have only a single electron gun which fires three rapid bursts at each set of three-color dots. The effect is essentially the same.)

The screen in a color tube is considerably more sophisticated than that used in a black-and-white unit. Its tiny dots are clustered into recurring groups of three different phosphorescent materials. One dot is red-yellow; another, green; the third, blue. The overall effect, however, is that of full, life-like color.

When you twiddle around with the controls of your color TV set, you can emphasize—or minimize—any one of the three colors, making the video image appear more red-yellow, more green or more blue.

How can the three primary colors of light be used to create so many other colors and hues? By their addition and subtraction. With high-quality color equipment, almost any color tint or hue can be blended from these three primary colors. For example, purple results when you add red-yellow and blue in the correct proportions. Subtract some of the red-yellow from the purple and you have lavender.

Color video doesn't actually mix the primary colors as a painter might on a palette. It "relates" them to the eye in those three-dot groupings and the human eye does the mixing. The eye sees purple when the red-yellow and blue dots shine brightly while the green stays dark.

If you look at a color video picture through a good strong magnifying glass, you'll see the myriad of blending color dots rather clearly.

VIDEO TECHNOLOGY has advanced to the point where there are now as many VCRs in homes across the country as there were TV sets just 30 years ago. More about these developments are in the article **VCR's Expanding Universe.**

HOW VIDEO IS STORED

When engineers tried to record television signals, they were confronted with a rather tricky problem. How could they get all the information on whatever recording medium they used?

In the very early days (way back in the 1950s), this could only be done by filming a video display tube. The resulting *kinescope* was of very poor quality. A more satisfactory answer had to be found in the magnetic tape recording that was then developing in sophistication for audio.

Audio recording

In conventional audio recording, plastic tape with a special metallic oxide is run by a head with an electromagnet in it. The varying voltage pattern of the audio frequencies changes the magnetic intensity in the head, and the pattern is passed on to the particles on the tape. Each cycle of voltage variation is written on the tape in a linear sequence as it passes by the head. In high-fidelity sound patterns, these voltages can change as many as 15,000 to 20,000 times a second. Each needs to be put on an unused part of the tape. The solution to getting that much audio information on a tape seemed simple: Move the tape past the head as fast as possible so there is always a clean, unused spot waiting for the head to record the next part of the voltage variation pattern in each cycle.

Audio recording technology in the 1950s required tape speeds of 15 inches per second. Even then the number of cycles that could be recorded was far fewer than the 15,000 to 20,000 we associate with high-fidelity sound reproduction because the gap between the magnetic poles in the head was so wide. Older vacuum tube technology, too, could not react quickly enough to change the magnetic field in the head as fast as it needed to be done. Advances in both machining and electronics allowed engineers to narrow that head gap and speed up the reaction of the electronic circuits. This increased the effective writing speed because it took less space on the tape to magnetically write the signal. Instead of moving the tape fast enough to write with a marking crayon, changing to the finely sharpened pencil point of a smaller head gap didn't require a clean space on the tape quite so fast. Now we can record on audio cassettes only 15/100-inch wide moving past the head at only 1.78 inches per second.

Video recording

But getting 20,000 cycles of voltage variations a second on a magnetic tape was nowhere near the challenge of the video signal that has over 4 million of these cycles each second. Even with the microscopically thin heads and quick-acting solid-state electronics, the tape would have to travel 200 times as fast. This means we'd need 200 times as much tape to record 60 minutes of video information as we do now to record an hour of sound. Carrying around—and marketing—reels of ¼-inch tape over 5 feet in diameter did not arouse much enthusiasm.

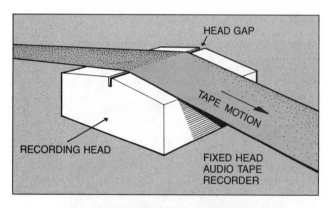

IN AUDIO RECORDING, the tape is moved past a stationary head. An electromagnet in the head changes the way oxide particles on the tape are arranged, storing sound patterns for later playback. High-frequency response depends on rapid tape motion, a small head gap and highly responsive electronic circuits.

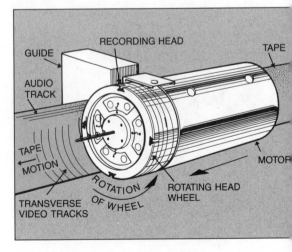

THE TRANSVERSE, quadraplex videotape recording put four recording heads on a drum that sent the output of each, from top to bottom, across a 2-in. tape.

To the engineers the answer (eventually) was obvious. In addition to moving the tape past the head, why not also move the heads in relation to the tape. By using a head spinning at right angles to the tape, the signal could be put down in narrow tracks from the top of the tape to the bottom. And, by using tape 2 inches wide, one complete line of information from a field of scanned video information could be recorded on each pass. This transverse scanning of the tape (instead of audio's longitudinal scanning) increased the effective length of the tape enormously. Each 2-inch top-to-bottom track takes up only a small fraction of an inch of longitudinal space on the tape. To slow down the speed at which the head was required to spin, a drum with four heads was

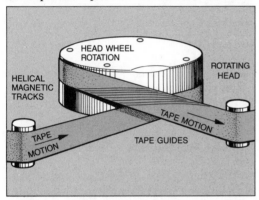

A HELICAL VIDEOTAPE HEAD confronts the passing tape at a slant, so the recorded signals are laid out along the tape in diagonal bands.

used. Each head lays down a virtually perfect vertical band of magnetized video signals across the tape. Recording the high-frequency demands of video was at last possible. For years this technology, called quadraplex (4 heads) transverse (top to bottom) recording, was the standard of the networks and broadcast stations—worldwide.

Helical VCRs

In less critical broadcast applications, and in the rapidly growing consumer marketplace for videocassette recorders (VCRs), a different kind of video recording is used. The *helical* recorder uses narrower tape, looped in a broad spiral around a large circular revolving head structure. This arrangement causes the video patterns to be laid down on the tape in a helical (or slanted track) configuration.

The two main videotape forms—transverse and helical—are not mutually compatible. Indeed, many different and incompatible formats have been developed within the helical category itself. VHS, Beta, U-Matic and 8mm are the more prominent of these.

WHERE VIDEO IS GOING

The relatively recent laser videodisc is a storage form of growing importance. Discs are encoded now at special manufacturing facilities. In this respect, they are akin to conventional records. Developments in ways for the user to write to a disc are so far advanced that any mention of their experimental nature is likely to be out of date before this article gets to the printer.

Technologically, the laser videodisc is a far cry from the grooved LP record. The videodisc depends on a small laser beam to write and read the video image information.

(An older form of grooved videodisc introduced to the market by RCA was discontinued in the mid 1980s. These CED machines no longer constitute an important technical format for future development.)

The modern videodisc is created by having a sophisticated laser-drive system etch microscopically tiny pits in the surface of a polished, rapidly revolving metal disc master. Each pit corresponds to a bit of the video image.

Digital video

In *conventional* video, picture scanning leads to an *analog* signal. This is an electrical wave form analogous to the density and color of each sampled dot in the original image.

In *digital* video, the scanning leads to a *binary* signal. Each sampled dot from the pickup tube yields a series of extremely fast electronic "on-offs"—or bits—which precisely describe, in multiple binary numbers, the voltage patterns needed to reproduce the image at that particular point in the scanning sequence.

The bits written by a laser on a videodisc at the factory can be read by a scanning laser placed in a videodisc player unit at home—or in a school or workplace. The laser beam, a sort of highly concentrated light ray, strikes the spiraling pits as they whiz by—at up to 1800 rpm—on the otherwise smooth surface of the spinning disc. (The metal disc itself has been carefully coated with a mirrored, glass-like acrylic finish to protect it from scratches.)

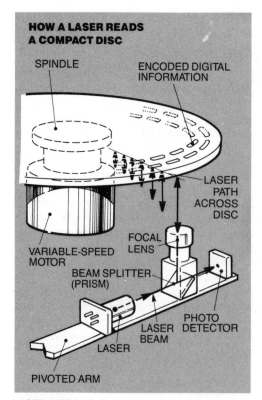

HOW A LASER READS A COMPACT DISC

SPINDLE

ENCODED DIGITAL INFORMATION

LASER PATH ACROSS DISC

VARIABLE-SPEED MOTOR

FOCAL LENS

BEAM SPLITTER (PRISM)

PHOTO DETECTOR

LASER BEAM

LASER

PIVOTED ARM

LASER DISCS used to record video operate in much the same way as the CD discs. Each pit in the surface of the disc sends back digital information which is decoded and interpreted as part of the color pattern of an image. Like the CD audio discs, videodiscs can be programmed for immediate and random access to any frame stored on it.

THE VIDEODISC can store millions of bits of information, making possible not only high-quality television pictures, but computer data bases of enormous capacity.

The laser is reflected back into an optical sensor. Each pit encountered momentarily interrupts the reflected beam. The optical sensor, therefore, receives binary "ons" (no pit) and "offs" (pit)—but in large numbers and extremely rapidly.

A single videodisc can store up to 54,000 frames of video information per side. Since each frame represents hundreds of thousands of sampled dots, there are millions of digital bits (including a good many for high-fidelity sound) on one disc. The videodisc is a modern marvel of high storage capacity.

Future of digital TV

A digital system is far more accurate and much less prone to distortion than an analog one. The future development of video equipment of all types, including TV receivers and recorders, is likely to be digital. Nowadays, most computers are digital. Audio is moving swiftly in that same technological direction. Just note the little digitally encoded compact disc (CD) which is techni-

cally related to the laser videodisc. It's already going great guns in the consumer marketplace. Several firms have announced plans to include still-frame video materials on CD discs. There is also at least one machine on the market which will play both the laser videodiscs and the CD music discs.

The laser disc is also used to archive binary data for computers in a much more efficient way than the floppy diskettes. One side of a laser videodisc can store the equivalent of some 12,700 diskettes! This entire set of the *Popular Mechanics Do-It-Yourself Encyclopedia* could be stored as a computer data base on a laser disc with plenty of room left over.

Technologists indicate that within a few years laser videodiscs will be made to behave like videotape. You'll be able to erase and record digital video at home on machines costing about what analog VCRs do now.

There are already production models of this technology in commercial applications. One version of the recordable videodisc uses a blue argon laser to write and a red helium-neon laser to read. The disc's surface is formulated to be highly absorptive to the argon laser so information can be written; at the same time, however, it must also be highly reflective to the helium-neon laser so the recorded information can be read. Most videodisc units on the general market now use similar helium-neon lasers, so any disc recorded by this new process is compatible with any player.

An earlier attempt to produce a recordable videodisc used a laser to heat the plastic surface of a disc and form its own new pits in the disc.

TV's third generation

■ IN THE BEGINNING, there were vacuum tubes and black and white pictures. The '60s brought solid-state transistor circuitry and afford-able color. Now, television's first and second generations are giving way to component monitors, monitor/receivers and high-resolution TV, and broadcasts have stereo sound. Digital circuitry improves imaging and gives new home sets screen within a screen, stop-action freeze frame and zoom focusing.

The switch to digital

Digital signal processing in the form of tiny, microprocessor chips is on the verge of replacing the conventional analog circuitry that now converts broadcast waveforms into sight and sound.

WITH NEW 20-INCH DIGITAL TV, a viewer can place an inset of the picture from another source in any corner of the screen.

How TV Resolution is Measured

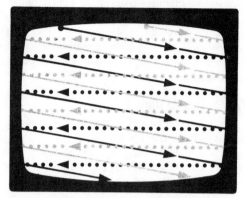

BROADCAST STANDARDS FIX TV's vertical resolution at 525 left-to-right lines running from top to bottom of screen. This 525-line frame is composed of two interlaced fields of 262½ lines each. Electron gun begins at top left corner of screen, zig-zags to create first field then races to top center to trace second field between lines of the first.

This application of computer technology to TV comes at a time when conventional methods are improving—and it's just a harbinger of things to come. Emerging beyond the digital horizon is High-Definition TV, which promises a wide, panoramic display and degree of clarity that rivals 70-mm movie film.

Digital television is the brainchild of ITT Intermetall of West Germany, and since 1983, about 50,000 sets have been sold in Europe and Japan. ITT's technology replaces the conventional TV's many wires and circuit boards with a handful of very large-scale integrated circuits similar to those employed in computers. The chips convert incoming video and audio signals to numerical values and store them in their computer memory for processing.

Once the signals become numbers, all manner of manipulation is possible. Special effects include superimposing a smaller, second picture on the main TV screen image. You can use the "picture-in-picture" (PIP) inset (¼ or ¹⁄₁₆ the main screen size) to monitor what your VCR is recording while you watch another broadcast program. The PIP also will freeze a frame from the main display for closer study. You can move the PIP to any corner of the screen. You can take portions of a freeze-frame and zoom-focus them to the full area of the screen.

While impressive, these effects do nothing to improve the basic TV image. But digital technology also can be used to correct colors, make ghosts more invisible and cancel distortion caused by outside interference (such as other electrical appliances or signal fluctuation caused by airplanes passing overhead). The chips can even be programmed to monitor the TV's operation, making internal adjustments to maintain consistent performance as parts age.

One of the more confusing designations applied to TV sets today is the term *monitor*. What makes it different from the conventional TV is its ability to route external video signals (from a VCR, for example) directly to the screen via input jacks, bypassing the tuner (or RF) stage.

With a conventional TV, you'd have to connect the external source to the antenna terminals for reception through the tuner. This means the video signal must be converted to radio frequencies (RF). In effect, your VCR, videodisc player or computer broadcasts to the TV. Any conversion of signals adds distortion along the way, degrading the image somewhat. Direct connections via jacks avoid this. A true component monitor, in fact, houses only the TV screen and video circuitry. To receive broadcast TV, you'd have to add a separate component tuner. You'd also need an amplifier and loudspeakers to project sound. The newly coined term "monitor/receiver" describes a monitor (direct video inputs) with TV tuner, amp and speakers in one chassis.

Despite its high-tech connotation, the word monitor doesn't guarantee video resolution superior to the common TV. Image quality can vary, and you only have "high-resolution" TV when you've got good specs. In TV, as in hi-fi, some published specifications can't be used for comparison because different manufacturers make their measurements differently. The specs you *can* rely on for TV are overscan, horizontal resolution and vertical resolution.

Overscan

Overscan is a design characteristic that causes some percentage of the picture area to be projected beyond the edges of a TV screen. It's meant to compensate for drops in electrical power, which cause the overall picture to shrink, and often frame the image area with a dark border. Thanks to hefty built-in power supplies, the best TVs need project only 5 or 6 percent of the image beyond your view. The lower the overscan percentage, the better. Inferior TVs hide as much as 18 percent of the picture from your view, to compensate for puny built-in power supplies that can't ride out a brown-out. Look for that low 5 or 6 percent overscan spec.

Horizontal resolution

Perhaps the most important specification with regard to TV image definition is horizontal resolution. This is expressed in lines, and determines a unit's ability to separate closely spaced details that appear beside one another. It's measured by projecting vertical stripe patterns of varying number onto a picture tube, then counting how many stripes are visible before they become so narrow and close together that they appear to merge into a solid span of gray. The more lines, the better. In some rare instances, you'll see horizontal resolution measured in megahertz (MHz). To translate this to lines, multiply the figure preceding MHz (as in 4.2 MHz) by 80. Thus, $4.2 \times 80 = 336$ lines.

Today's "hi-res" TVs have 330 to 350 or more lines of horizontal resolution, compared to about 250 in a conventional TV. They achieve this not by digital wizardry, but by comb filters and by fine-pitch tube designs that enable more picture elements to hit the screen. With regard to pitch, think of the dots that make up a newspaper photograph. The more dots, the more detailed the picture. Comb filters aid resolution by separating the color information from the black-and-white (contrast and brightness) information, before projecting them on the screen. This preserves much of the original picture definition carried in the broadcast signal, yielding higher fidelity reproduction.

Vertical resolution

Vertical resolution is often confused with horizontal resolution, but it's not a TV specification. It's a broadcasting standard set in the early days of telecasting and still used in the United States and elsewhere.

Measured from the top of your screen to the bottom, there are 525 lines that make up a picture. Actually, the picture is composed of two interlaced fields of 262½ lines each, which follow one another by 1/60th of a second.

This 525-line standard does limit TV's vertical resolution—that is, its ability to reproduce fine details that appear above and below one another on the screen. Because it's a broadcast standard, filters and improved fine-pitch tubes can't be used to increase the number of vertical lines as they can for horizontal lines. To do this, the broadcast transmission method would have to be changed. An easier solution would be to use digital technology to increase vertical resolution at the TV receiver—and that's the path some TV manufacturers are now pursuing.

From hi-res to high definition

When you can get 1,050 to 1,125 lines of vertical resolution, projected on a wider screen with 5-to-3 width-to-height ratio (compared to the current 4-to-3 ratio), that's High Definition TV (HDTV).

DIGITAL SIGNAL PROCESSING offers a way to increase TV's vertical resolution without altering broadcast standards. Shown above is a computer graphic photographed from 14-inch, high-resolution monitor. Left side of image depicts TV in normal 525-line vertical scanning mode. Right side of graphic shows effect of digital doublescanning—1,050 lines. Digital process interpolates missing information between each of 525 regular vertical scanning lines for higher definition and a flicker-free image. The horizontal resolution is identical for each side of the graphic: The tube will project about 350 lines.

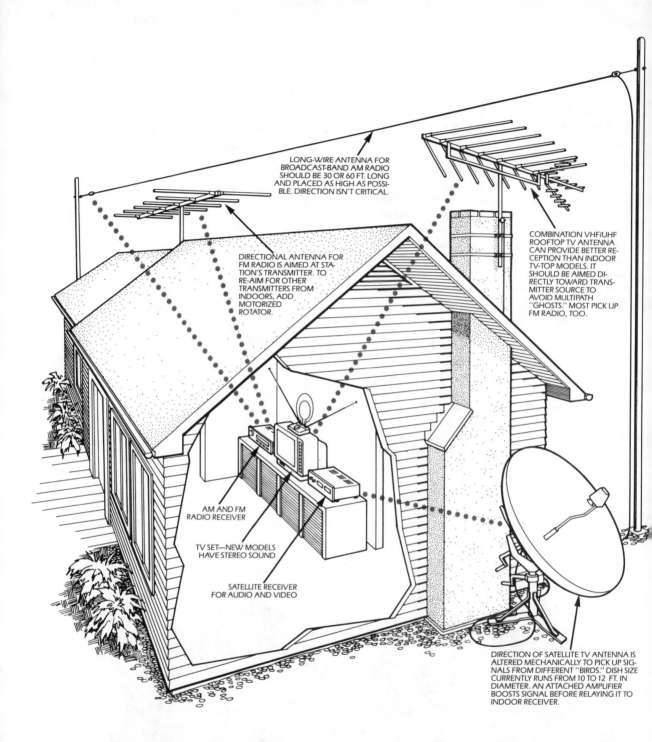

LONG-WIRE ANTENNA FOR BROADCAST-BAND AM RADIO SHOULD BE 30 OR 60 FT. LONG AND PLACED AS HIGH AS POSSIBLE. DIRECTION ISN'T CRITICAL.

COMBINATION VHF/UHF ROOFTOP TV ANTENNA CAN PROVIDE BETTER RECEPTION THAN INDOOR TV-TOP MODELS. IT SHOULD BE AIMED DIRECTLY TOWARD TRANSMITTER SOURCE TO AVOID MULTIPATH "GHOSTS." MOST PICK UP FM RADIO, TOO.

DIRECTIONAL ANTENNA FOR FM RADIO IS AIMED AT STATION'S TRANSMITTER. TO RE-AIM FOR OTHER TRANSMITTERS FROM INDOORS, ADD MOTORIZED ROTATOR.

AM AND FM RADIO RECEIVER

TV SET—NEW MODELS HAVE STEREO SOUND

SATELLITE RECEIVER FOR AUDIO AND VIDEO

DIRECTION OF SATELLITE TV ANTENNA IS ALTERED MECHANICALLY TO PICK UP SIGNALS FROM DIFFERENT "BIRDS." DISH SIZE CURRENTLY RUNS FROM 10 TO 12 FT. IN DIAMETER. AN ATTACHED AMPLIFIER BOOSTS SIGNAL BEFORE RELAYING IT TO INDOOR RECEIVER.

Tv antenna selection

■ BEFORE YOU GO STORMING back to the retailer who sold you an apparently defective TV set next time you get a lousy picture on it, consider this. Mother Nature and modern man have conspired to place a variety of obstacles in the path of the broadcast pictures and sound waves searching for your home receiver. No matter how expensive or sensitive your TV or radio receiver is, it can't perform any better than the electrical signal it's receiving. The old computer maxim applies: Garbage in, garbage out.

You can help those signals find their way home by selecting the right antenna, installing it properly and maintaining it in top condition. Installation and maintenance are important. If you're on the fringe area of radio or TV stations, expect bad reception if your antenna is rusty, has poor mechanical connections or is pointed in the wrong direction.

Because of recent or pending changes in the quality of broadcast programming, now is as good a time as any to take a close look at your antenna with an eye to upgrading reception.

Soundwise, many FM stereo stations are adding the new laser-read, digital compact discs to their on-air repertoire. A good antenna will help you pick up these noise-free, full dynamic range recordings with no transmission-related fuzziness or fading. Broadcast TV's ready to go stereo too, as is AM radio. If you're planning to buy an up-to-date receiver to pick up the new sound dimension, it will pay to invest in a good antenna at the same time.

On the video side of the picture, a new generation of TVs uses digital circuitry *within* the receiver to process and improve the received analog broadcast signal. Moreover, at least one manufacturer, is now building TV sets that process the full color signal transmitted by the broadcaster. Other manufacturers probably will add this feature before long, and begin to incorporate it into videocassette recorder tuner sections, too. With these innovations in mind, it only makes sense to feed your TV all the signal you can.

In choosing and installing an antenna, it pays to follow these tips:

First, antennas are cut for specific frequency ranges—FM, VHF, UHF. Make sure the one you buy covers the stations you want to receive. Second, the feed line that connects the antenna to your receiver must match the receiver's impedance rating. This figure should be listed in your owner's manual, or on the back of the set. Finally, for optimal reception, all connections and connectors should be kept free of rust and corrosion. Also, make sure the feed line has no cracks or breaks.

With this said, it's time to look at the antenna options you have.

Outdoor television antennas

An outdoor TV antenna must deal with signals in two different frequency ranges—VHF and

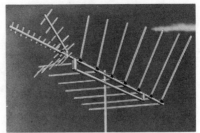

MOST ROOFTOP TV ANTENNAS combine VHF (long elements) and UHF (short elements).

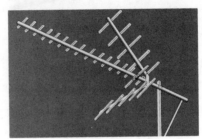

UHF-ONLY ANTENNAS also can be roof-mounted for improving difficult reception.

UHF. These signals act somewhat alike, but differ in their received power levels. VHF signals tend to carry farther from a transmitting tower than UHF. Accordingly, a television set that receives VHF frequencies well (stations 2 through 13) might have trouble with UHF (stations 14 through 83).

To solve this problem a UHF antenna has to be more sensitive than the VHF. It also must have an additional component—a reflector or collector element. Acting somewhat like a mirror, this component collects signals and assembles them at a central point on the antenna before relaying them to the TV.

For the television owner who wants the best possible reception on all bands, the way to go is with a directional beam antenna that includes a reflector or collector element. Many outdoor antennas on the market combine elements for both VHF and UHF reception. Moreover, most of these also can be used to improve reception on your FM radio or stereo receiver since the entire FM radio band is situated between VHF stations 6 and 7.

Keep in mind that a single antenna can feed more than one receiver, including your videocassette recorder's tuner section. All you need do is connect the antenna lead (wire) to the required number of band separators and signal splitters, which then route the signals to the proper receivers.

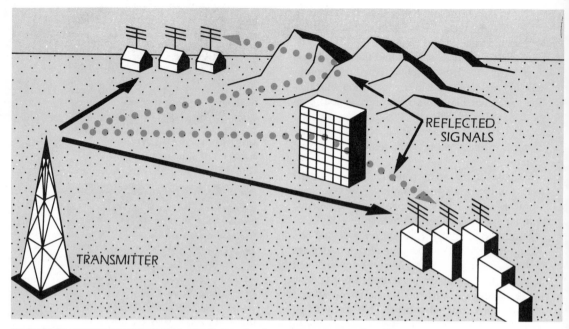

TV GHOSTS AND FUZZY FM SOUND (multipath distortions) occur when signals arrive at the receiver after the direct signal. A well-aimed antenna alleviates this problem.

Indoor television antennas

Although an outdoor antenna placed as high as possible is the best way to go, many apartment dwellers must use indoor antennas to pick up broadcast TV. Television signals act much like FM radio signals and are subject to difficulties caused by terrain, buildings and the way they interact with the Earth. In this situation, the indoor television antenna users needs all the help they can get.

An indoor antenna capable of directivity is the ticket. That is, you should be able to rotate the elements and fine-tune the antenna for the strongest signal. A curtain-type of antenna for UHF is also very effective. Both of these alternatives offer marked improvements over the traditional rabbit ears found on the backs of television sets.

Television signals pose another problem because they operate in two slices of the radio spectrum—VHF and UHF. Both are affected by the same types of problems. However, UHF poses still a further problem. Because the wavelength of the signal is relatively short, something as seemingly harmless as a tree branch or nearby telephone pole may cause problems with receiving a station's signal. Thus, a directional type antenna is the answer here, too. This type of antenna is probably familiar to most television users. It combines a movable center loop with the traditional rabbit ears into a single television-top unit.

When all else fails, try adding a signal ampli-

fier. This device takes a weak signal and boosts it electronically. The amplifier may be installed either at the front end of the antenna lead or at the end of the cable where it connects to the TV set.

Satellite reception

There's an interesting phenomenon going on in this country—satellite television. Nearly a million satellite dishes are now in place in back yards all around the United States. By aiming an antenna at a geostationary Earth satellite, you can

INDOOR TV ANTENNA come in a variety of shapes and types. Although most combine VHF and UHF functions, UHF-only antennas (such as the curtain model, left) also are available. The most effective rabbit ears antennas (model at right) let you fine-tune to get the best VHF signal. UHF reception also is enhanced by directional models that let you rotate the center loops to receive the strongest signal possible.

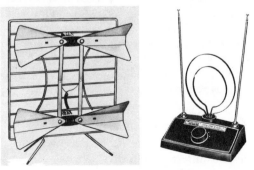

THE SATELLITE DISH picks up many channels.

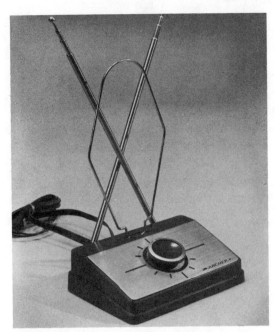

INDOOR FM ANTENNA looks like the TV type.

receive a great deal of programming not otherwise available from your local TV broadcaster. Besides the various pay TV channels, many of the major television services transmit signals to those satellites for retransmission to other areas of the country.

The optimum antenna for this type of reception is the 3-meter (about 10 feet) dish. It looks much like the traditional radar antenna, and is, in fact, much like it. At the center of the dish, located at the prime focal point, is what is known as an LNA or low-noise amplifier. This picks up the minuscule amount of satellite signal actually reaching Earth, and boosts it before sending it on to the satellite TV receiver and TV set located indoors. A satellite receiver looks much like a regular stereo receiver. It lets you tune in on a satellite transmission, then relays the audio and video information to your TV.

The reason the LNA is called "low noise" is because it relays the signal with little distortion, so that the receiver and television set get all the signal possible. A satellite antenna also requires a very specialized, low-loss type of connector cable and precise placement to perform well. Although install-it-yourself kits are available, many people hire a professional surveyor to site the dish properly in relation to the satellite positions.

Indoor FM reception

Because of the transmission characteristics in the VHF portion of the spectrum where FM radio stations are located (between channels 6 and 7), specialized antennas are needed. These antennas must help overcome multipath losses, reflections and polarization changes.

Multipath losses occur because VHF signals tend to bounce around. They are affected by such things as trees and buildings, and two or more signals may arrive at an antenna at the same time and confuse the FM receiver. The result is fuzzy sound. The antenna you want is one that will latch onto and hold the strongest signal, while rejecting multipath signals.

Another reason why weak FM broadcast signals have a fading in-and-out quality is that the antenna also must handle signals which are coming to it at many angles. This called a polarization problem. For indoors, perhaps the best antenna would be the directional type. It offers you the chance to fine-tune for strongest reception. Another alternative is the simple two-element dipole antenna. Available from any electronics shop and included with many FM receivers, this is the basic directional antenna. Turning it should clean up reception.

Another good alternative is a version of an old radio favorite, the minicurtain antenna. This type of antenna offers more receiving area than other types of indoor FM receiving antennas. It has two bow ties which serve to focus received signals, and looks much like a cake rack with bow ties attached.

Outdoor FM reception

FM receivers and antennas must deal with tricky signal characteristics, and it's wise to use a

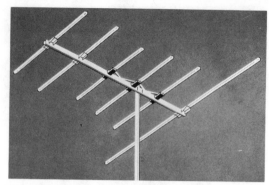

FM RECEPTION is best with an outdoor beam.

beam-type of antenna. These offer great sensitivity and the ability to pull in a strong signal from a mishmash of radio waves.

Because the FM frequency is VHF, it's quite possible to have as many as seven or more elements on an outdoor FM antenna. This means it will be successful at pulling in distant signals. But, as more elements are added to the beam, the narrower its aim becomes. Thus, you will find that with only a little misaiming, the signal you had hoped to find has disappeared to be replaced by

another. It will require re-aiming this antenna to get the signal back.

You will need some sort of rotator mechanism to change antenna direction from indoors. This is especially true if your favorite stations are located on all points of the compass. Rotators, mechanical or electrical, can be expensive. Instead, supplement your permanently oriented outdoor antenna with an indoor model you can fine-tune.

AM broadcast band

In the winter, because of certain atmospheric conditions, it's sometimes possible to hear AM stations thousands of miles away. The best way to do this is with a long wire antenna 30 or 60 feet long and placed as high and as clear of obstructions as possible. For the apartment-bound, the ferrite-bar antenna located on the back of most hi-fi receivers should improve reception when rotated.

Although AM signals carry over long distances, sonic fidelity has never been considered important because voices and music are transmitted monoaurally. Now that more AM stations are switching over to stereo broadcasts, a good antenna coupled to an AM stereo receiver will enhance your music listening pleasure.

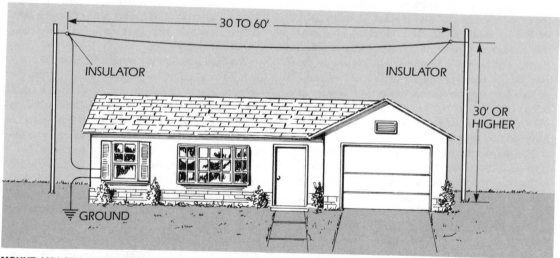

MOUNT AM LONG WIRE ANTENNA as high as possible, using insulators to couple the line to uprights. Run line to the receiver, and attach receiver to an appropriate ground.

TV antenna installation

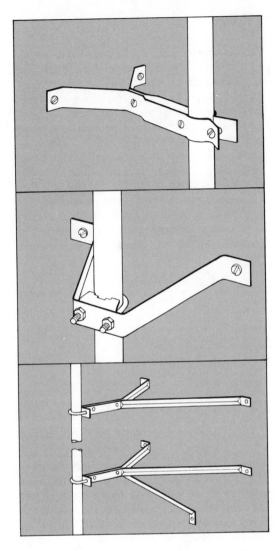

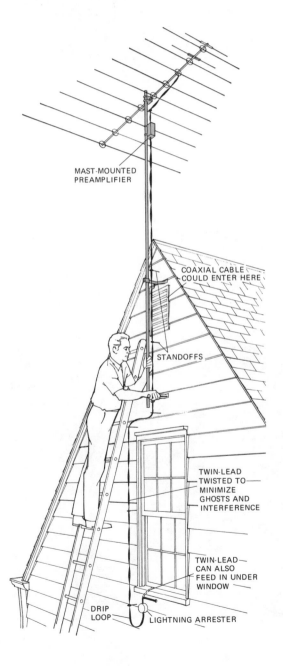

MAST-MOUNTED PREAMPLIFIER

COAXIAL CABLE COULD ENTER HERE

STANDOFFS

TWIN-LEAD TWISTED TO MINIMIZE GHOSTS AND INTERFERENCE

TWIN-LEAD CAN ALSO FEED IN UNDER WINDOW

DRIP LOOP

LIGHTNING ARRESTER

Gable mount must clear eaves

Techniques start with the right mount. Above: three types of wall mount; pick a pair deep enough to clear your eaves' overhang. Mount them at least 2 ft. apart for masts up to 10 ft.; for 15-ft. mast height, use three brackets, 2 ft. apart, and a 20-ft. mast. Coaxial cable is the best lead-in, unless you have very weak signals and no ghosts or interference; if you use flat twin-lead (it's cheaper), twist it once per foot to reduce ghost and noise pickup. Keep twin-lead well away from metal, or from surfaces which may get wet.

Chimney mounts avoid roof-walking

Chimney mount is popular and easy, if the chimney's at least 3 feet high, made of real brick, and in good condition. Check for loose bricks and chipped mortar. Use sturdy mounts, with heavy-duty, rustproof hardware and brackets, stainless-steel straps. Smoke corrodes, so if chimney is active, use color-anodized steel masts, 75-ohm antenna with screw-plug coaxial connections. Straps should be near top and bottom of chimney, 2½ to 4 ft. apart—the farther, the sturdier. Line up straps with brick rows to level them, attach mast brackets loosely before raising antenna to roof, align antenna mast with a level before tightening straps. No chimney? Use vent-pipe mount.

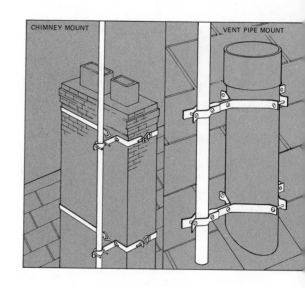

CHIMNEY MOUNT VENT PIPE MOUNT

Tripods are the most rigid roof mounts

Tripod mounts, unlike other roof mounts, need no guy wires for masts up to 5 ft. high; for taller masts requiring guys, base mounts (next page) are easier to install, cheaper. Eave-mounting tripod (below, left) has swivel mast support, so mast can be attached, swung into place, then fixed.

Tower type (below, right) adjusts for flat or peaked roofs. All roof (and wall) mounts should be attached to beams or masonry—never to unsupported roofing or siding, or mortar between bricks. To locate beams, tap with hammer, drive test nails where your roof feels most solid.

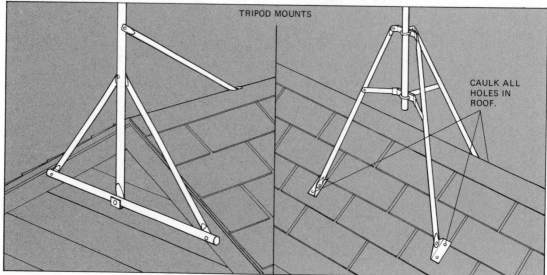

TRIPOD MOUNTS

CAULK ALL HOLES IN ROOF.

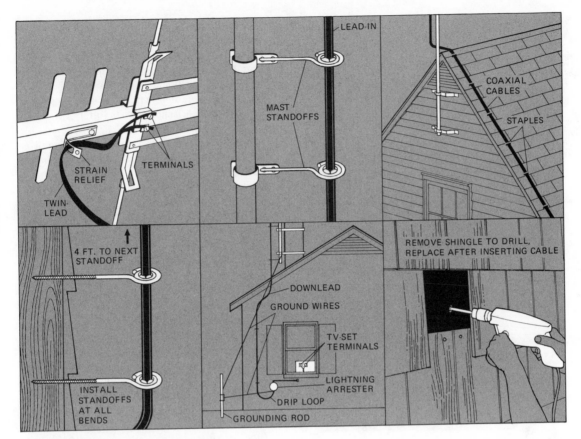

LEAD-IN

MAST STANDOFFS

COAXIAL CABLES

STAPLES

STRAIN RELIEF

TERMINALS

TWIN-LEAD

4 FT. TO NEXT STANDOFF

REMOVE SHINGLE TO DRILL, REPLACE AFTER INSERTING CABLE

DOWNLEAD

GROUND WIRES

TV-SET TERMINALS

INSTALL STANDOFFS AT ALL BENDS

LIGHTNING ARRESTER

DRIP LOOP

GROUNDING ROD

Wire it right for a better picture

Downlead should be wired to antenna and secured by a strain relief before antenna is raised. Flat twin-lead must be routed away from mast and building side with standoffs (leave enough slack between standoffs to allow for cold-weather contraction, wind, but not enough to let lead flap), and requires a lightning arrester where downlead enters house. Coaxial cables can be taped to mast, stapled to house (but be sure staples don't crush inner shield). Masts, lightning arresters, shield of coax must be grounded for safety. To keep wire entrance from leaking, form drip loop below it, drilling hole slightly upwards. Holes around a coaxial cable can be caulked, but waterproofing of twin-lead entrances requires special feedthrough hardware. To conceal and waterproof a hole in a shingle house, remove one shingle, drill the hole, then replace the shingle.

MORE TIPS:

☐ To aim antenna: (a) Use a compass and a pilot's map which shows antenna tower sites; (b) have someone watch set and report to you by walkie-talkie or "people chain" (easier if set is near a window); (c) put your set in the yard, where you can see it from your roof (but make sure set is grounded); (d) Take a battery-powered portable set (preferably color) to roof with you.

☐ If putting antenna on a rotor, leave enough slack in leads at the top for rotor to turn without breaking the downlead.

☐ Coaxial cable and quality twin-lead can last 10 years; cheap twin-lead can go in 2.

☐ For inconspicuous entry, bring leads into house at baseboard level, in a closet, or just below a window.

☐ If you must staple twin-lead indoors, drive staples parallel to conductors, as closely centered between them as possible.

☐ Leave slack where the downlead meets the set, so you can move the set for cleaning, or repair. The slack in coaxial cable can be coiled—but twin-lead should never be coiled, just left slack.

TYPICAL ROOF-MOUNT ANTENNA —this one is a TravelSat dish—is deployed for reception.

Satellite TV hits the road

NEARLY A MILLION American households now enjoy more than 100 channels of TV entertainment received through large satellite dish antennas planted in their backyards. The latest development in this exciting technology lets owners of motor homes take their favorite satellite programs on vacation.

With a dish antenna mounted on roof or bumper, the TV set in your motor home will always have a picture. No matter how many miles you put between yourself and civilization's nearest transmitter tower, you'll never drive beyond range of the nearly 20 birds that beam movies, sports, news and music to the North American continent.

Dish antennas designed for a stationary installation have diameters as large as 12 feet. The bigger the dish, the more signal it can collect from more satellites. This is especially important if you live on the coasts, because satellite signals are strongest at the geographic center of the continental United States.

By necessity, the dishes made for motor homes span a manageable 4 to 6 feet. This means you'll have to rough it a bit in the wilds, and scoop your signal from the relatively new generation of high-powered satellites. A handful of these 9-watt and 7½-watt replays have gone aloft in recent years to supplement older 5-watt birds launched when 16-foot dishes were not uncommon.

Even so, you won't lack for programming diversity. For example, up to 24 channels of entertainment are available from the Galaxy I satellite alone, one of the new high-wattage birds. Selections include Home Box Office, Cinemax, The Movie Channel, Showtime, Cable News Network, ESPN (all sports), Black Entertainment Television, Spanish International Network, The Disney Channel and the Nashville Network—and more. Additional high-power birds are scheduled for launch over the next few years, so it's not likely that the mobile dish you buy today will ever lack employment.

Many of these entertainment services are now scrambling their satellite signals to prevent unauthorized viewing. Their programming is still available to you, however, simply by contacting them and subscribing to the service. There are still an abundance of free, unscrambled signals available to the motor home with a satellite dish.

Types of rigs

There are two installation approaches to satellite TV for motor homes. One is the bumper-mounted dish, which you set up on the ground and aim ("sight" in satellite jargon) manually on the satellite of your choice. The second type of dish installation is permanently mounted on the motor home's roof, and sighted by remote control from within the van. The difference between the two is substantial, at least where cost and installation are concerned.

The least expensive approach is a 50-pound dish, 5 feet in diameter. The dish can be set up manually in a few minutes, and is connected to the satellite receiver inside the van. When not in use, the dish is transported on a bumper mount in the rear.

A few days spent deploying and sighting a bumper-mount dish by hand will let you appreciate the benefits of a rooftop installation. The dish is always in place, and a remote-control device called an actuator enables you to sight the dish by pushbutton while monitoring the results on your television screen.

Installation

Lightweight, bumper-mounted manual systems are tailor-made for the do-it-yourself installer. Assembly's no tougher than putting a ski or bike rack on your car. Roof installations are another matter.

DISH, ROTATION AND ELEVATION
mechanisms put great weight on an RV's
roof. Wind loading adds stress. Horizontal
aluminum bars (above) distribute the
burden.

Mounting a dish on the roof of a motor home isn't a one-person job. Installing a rooftop satellite system is an all-day job. Figure at least two hours for dish assembly alone if it's a mesh antenna you must construct from grapefruit-like sections. Another three hours will be spent in securing the dish and the motor assembly to the roof.

Although manufacturers supply the basic hardware you'll need to attach the dish and rotating mechanism to your motor home's roof, some suggest installation procedures that go a bit further. The best (read "safest") installations call for a pair of aluminum bars, bolted to the roof as mounting channels for your dish. The bars help distribute the weight and stress more evenly than would be the case if you bolted the dish assembly directly to the roof.

This is very sound advice, when you consider that a dish assembly can weigh as much as 250 pounds, and will be transported at highway speeds. In fact, some dish and motor home manufacturers say this type of reinforcement is a must for motor homes built before 1982, and for certain pull trailers. The aluminum mounting channels aren't supplied with the dish package, but you can buy them from satellite dish and recreational vehicle dealers. By the way, never attempt to drive your motor home with the dish in anything but the storage position. Even a mesh antenna reacts to wind loading like a solid object at speeds over 30 mph. For this reason, all roof-mount dishes collapse flat to the motor home roof.

Tuning-in the heavens

Once your satellite dish is on-line and in the field, scooping the signals from different satellites can make you feel like a starship navigator. For the roving vacationer who is potentially in different territory every evening, an old-fashioned compass broken down into 1° increments is a necessary item.

Actual sighting procedures vary according to the type of equipment you've installed.

Typically, to locate a specific satellite you must first take the compass heading of the motorhome dish, and add 160°. Next, add the magnetic deviation for your location, as described in the manufacturer's viewing guide. (If the total is more then 360°, subtract 360°.) This is the number you'll punch into the actuator keyboard—the actuator and dish motor do the rest. If your dish is of the bumper-mount, manually sighted type, you'll get some exercise that you might find welcome after a long drive.

If you're willing to live with the smaller but ample selection of programming from the higher-powered satellites, there are plenty of accessories available to bring the picture to your living room television. With a bit of planning, you can turn a one-dish TV supper into a movable feast.

EASY INSTALLATION and deployment is
the strong suit of lightweight, manually
sighted bumper-mount dishes. So is price.

ROOF-MOUNT DISHES have the
advantage of height to help see over
obstacles such as trees. They also have
remote-control sighting.

TV interference problems

1 Weak signal—grainy, degraded

5 Ghosts—multiple imaging

Weak TV signals

These can be mistaken for television-interference (TVI) problems. If all channels have the same grainy, degraded appearance, look for corroded or broken connections all along the lead-in cable, from the antenna to the TV set. This type of maintenance is indicated if you formerly had good reception. If you have never had satisfactory picture quality, you may need a better antenna, or the existing antenna should be placed higher up and perhaps be fitted with a signal amplifier for improved reception.

If only one or two channels have the overall grainy appearance, your cable connections are probably in good shape. Perhaps you are simply located in a fringe area with respect to the particular channels affected. Better antenna orientation (direction and height) and use of a signal amplifier should solve the problem.

Electrical interference

If very pronounced, this might be mistaken for a weak signal condition, although the two effects are actually quite easy to differentiate. A weak signal causes uniform degradation of the entire picture area. On the other hand, even severe electrical TVI tends to form changing bands of flickering, short, horizontal lines, or else more randomly spaced, bright pinpoints of white light. The latter effect is very common when an electrical storm is in the viewing area.

If you observe pinpoints of light dancing around on the screen when there is a breeze blowing outside but no storm, check the lead-in wire connections to the antenna. Odds are you will find at least one connection either badly corroded or broken off.

To track down other intermittent electrical TVI, go around the house and turn off operating appliances one by one.

If a portable radio is affected by the same interference, carry it around your home area and see where it sounds noisiest. It's just possible that you will get loudest radio interference when you move closer and closer to your neighbors' property; maybe their appliance or engine is creating the problem.

If the interference is caused by a power drill or saw, you may live with the minor nuisance. However, any appliance that causes persistently annoying disruption of TV or stereo equipment performance should be corrected (see illustration).

FM radio interference

This can be caused by a nearby FM broadcast station and may create a herringbone pattern that is easy to confuse with a similar pattern caused by misadjustment of the TV set's fine-tuning control. If the tuning control is at fault, the interference pattern fluctuates with sound changes in the TV program; if FM interference is present, the pattern fluctuates with variations in the sound of the FM broadcast, *not* with the sound of the TV program.

FM TVI is usually most bothersome on Chan-

2 Electrical—bands of snow

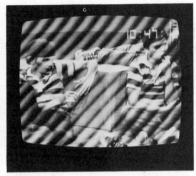

3 FM radio—hash-like stripes

4 Computer—similar to radio

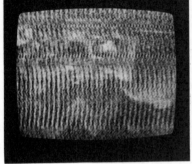

6 CB radio—pulsing lines

7 Co-channel—different images

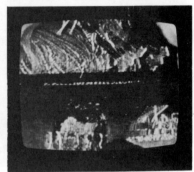

8 Airplanes—picture tears

nel 6, although other channels in the 2 to 13 series may also be affected. Before attempting a cure, make certain that the FM interference is not caused by a nearby FM *receiver*.

To become familiar with FM interference, hold a portable FM receiver near a TV set tuned to Channel 13. Dial the radio down to the 96- to 97-megahertz range and observe the variety of interference patterns on the screen.

If your own FM receiver is the problem, just move it a little farther away from the TV set. If the FM TVI is caused by a broadcast station, start by installing an inexpensive FM-band rejection filter at the rear of the TV set. Connect the filter to the antenna leads as instructed in the literature that comes with it. Use a connector cable of the same type as the existing antenna lead. This may be a simple twin-lead wire or a coaxial cable; just don't mix the two types.

If you have an antenna amplifier, install one filter before the amplifier and a second one ahead of the TV receiver input terminals. You may also be instructed to add a ground wire which should be kept as short as possible. If the filters don't solve the problem, a service call may be needed for in-set modifications.

Computer-generated TVI

This is generally not a problem unless the computer is quite close to the TV set. During our tests, Channels 2, 4 and 13 were found to be most sensitive to computer radiation. However, the radiation put out by some other computer might affect a TV set differently, perhaps on other channels, and produce other types of interference patterns.

If neighbors buy a hobby computer, don't be in a rush to blame them for all your TV interference problems. It's simple enough to check it out by turning the computer on and off while watching the TV set. Not all computers create TVI, even when operated next to the television receiver.

Ghosting

This is a formation of double images and occurs when the TV signal travels along two paths of different lengths from the broadcast tower to a receiving antenna. However, ghosting can also be caused by a poor TV antenna and/or lead-in wire, or merely improper aiming of a directional-type antenna. Check these possibilities first.

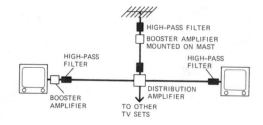

HIGH-PASS FILTER
BOOSTER AMPLIFIER
MOUNTED ON MAST
HIGH-PASS FILTER
HIGH-PASS FILTER
BOOSTER AMPLIFIER
DISTRIBUTION AMPLIFIER
TO OTHER TV SETS

If the problem obviously relates to multipath reception of a reflected signal, try moving the antenna to a different location. If that doesn't cure the problem, replace the antenna with a more directional type, and be sure to use shielded-type lead-in wire.

CB radio interference

This can be caused by citizens band and amateur "ham" radio transmissions, but also by transmissions by police and other public service radios.

Such TVI characteristically occurs in the form of dark parallel lines tilted slightly off the horizontal. These patterns are easy to confuse with similar effects caused by horizontal-hold problems in the TV set. But these aren't the only interference patterns produced by radio transmitters.

The actual effects vary greatly depending on many factors, including the strength of the radio signal and whether the radio operator is actually talking or merely sending out an unmodulated carrier wave.

If the TVI is, in fact, due to radio interference, the pattern will pulsate as the radio operator talks, and may even bounce back and forth between the parallel-line pattern and more random patterns.

You will not observe such pulsations if the parallel lines are caused by horizontal-hold problems; instead you may hear a high-pitched tone. To cure a hold malfunction, readjust the horizontal-hold control. If that doesn't work, have a serviceman replace a bad component.

Eliminating radio transmitter TVI can be a problem. You should begin by installing an inexpensive high-pass filter at the antenna terminals of the TV set. Be sure to use the same type of connecting cable as is used for the antenna lead-in (either twin-lead wire or a coaxial cable). Put one filter ahead of an antenna signal amplifier you may be using and a second filter at the TV set.

If the filters don't cure the problem, you may need modifications of the TV set's circuits.

Co-channel images

This resembles ghosting, but is easily recognized because the second image is usually of a *different* program, which means it is coming from a second TV broadcast station. Remember, true ghosting involves a duplication of the same TV program material.

Co-channel interference is most commonly caused by atmospheric conditions that permit signals from a very distant station to bounce back down from the upper atmosphere and thereby "skip" to receiving areas they normally wouldn't reach. There's nothing to do about a temporary problem except wait until the atmospheric condition clears, usually within an hour or two.

However, if you experience *persistent* co-channel interference, it means that you are located where it is possible to pick up signals regularly from two broadcast stations on the same channel. You may be able to cure or minimize the problem by installing a highly directional antenna. If some interference persists, try reducing the signal strength with a tunable signal attenuator that actually weakens the signal getting into the TV set.

Airplanes and windmills

Here are but two examples of miscellaneous outside sources of TVI. The whirring blades of a helicopter or the wings of a banking 747 can cause TV interference. The display may tear badly, and there may be a temporary loss of color. The problem is really troublesome only near busy airports.

Some channels may be more sensitive than others to such disturbances, perhaps partly because of weak TV signals. The installation of a better antenna, use of a shielded coaxial lead-in cable, and addition of an antenna signal amplifier can greatly reduce the effects of aircraft.

A similar problem can be caused by windmills! People living in rural areas may already be familiar with this source of TVI.

Of course, there's also TVI that originates from malfunctioning equipment at the TV broadcast station, and the broadcaster usually—but not always—announces that fact. If you observe bad color or other picture distortions during the presentation of field-recorded news broadcasts, for example, it may be due simply to a malfunction or inexpert use of the broadcaster's portable camera equipment.

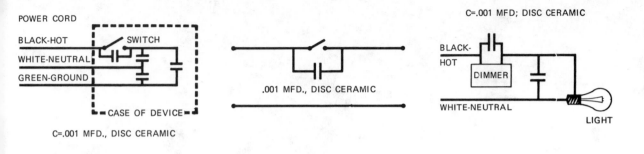

POWER CORD
BLACK-HOT
WHITE-NEUTRAL
GREEN-GROUND
SWITCH
CASE OF DEVICE
C=.001 MFD., DISC CERAMIC

.001 MFD., DISC CERAMIC

C=.001 MFD; DISC CERAMIC
BLACK-HOT
DIMMER
WHITE-NEUTRAL
LIGHT

HIGH-PASS FILTERS can be useful if installed as shown at far left. Don't forget to put one on each side of a booster amp. Try the three cures shown above to solve the interference from appliances or dimmer-switches—but be careful of a.c. wiring if you make modifications. See text for further instructions.

Additional tips

If a specific ham or CB transmitter in your area obviously relates to your TVI problem, work with the operator to check his equipment for proper performance. See if the rig is properly grounded, test for harmonics and/or spurious emissions, and add a good earth ground if the transmitter cabinet radiates energy. Install a *low-pass* filter on the transmitter antenna circuit to see if the TVI pattern is affected by changes in harmonics and/or spurious emissions.

Check antenna connections

If these measures fail, go back to the TV receiver and recheck all antenna connections. If there's an antenna signal amplifier, remove it temporarily. If this eliminates TVI, reconnect the amplifier, but protect it against radio frequency (RF) pickup as follows: 1. Add grounding; 2. enclose the amplifier in a metallic RF-proof housing and ground the housing; 3. install a high-pass filter at the input to the amplifier; 4. install a second such filter in series if the first one is not adequate.

Add a purchased a.c. power-line RF filter to determine if the RF from the transmitter is entering the TV set by way of the power cord. If the TVI persists, even when the antenna is disconnected, look for the problem inside the TV set, especially at the tuner. Disconnect the antenna input lead inside the set at the tuner. If the TVI is eliminated, install a high-pass filter at the tuner. If this doesn't cure the problem, each stage of the TV must be tested—a job for a repairman.

Electrical TVI caused by sparking home appliances and tools can often be eliminated by adding capacitor bypasses. *However, the modifications must be done with extreme care, especially when bypassing appliances having capacitors.* Dangerous voltages may exist, the a.c. power line might accidentally be shorted and an inexperienced do-it-yourselfer can invite electrocution!

Interference from tools

Arcing between the brushes and commutators of infrequently used power tools are best left alone. If the tools are in constant use, TVI can be reduced by bypassing each side of the line to the other side and to ground with capacitors. The on/off switch also should be bypassed.

Also, .001-mfd. capacitors may be used to bypass arcing contacts in such thermostatically controlled appliances as electric blankets and fish-tank heaters. Defective TVI-producing doorbell transformers should be replaced. Dimmer switches that utilize SCRs or triacs can cause much hard-to-eliminate TVI. However, bypassing with capacitors may help somewhat.

Expanding universe of VCRs

■ HOME VIDEO HAS TRAVELED light years since Sony introduced the first household recorders that could store TV programs for later viewing—or even turn the living room into a first run movie theater.

That original Betamax VCR would record a single hour of moving images on magnetic tape, accompanied by monaural sound with a good deal more hiss than the average phonograph record. Special features were limited: it could be programmed in advance to record a single show. The old LV-1901 cost $3,000 in 1975 and, because it was packaged with a 19-inch color TV, lugging it around to make videocamera movies was out of the question.

The latest generation of video recorders is a good deal more sophisticated in features and flexible in operation. There are also more choices—and more affordable prices.

Special picture effects once found only in the priciest models are now available across the board. For your ears, the newest and most advanced hi-fi VCRs can capture stereo sounds on a par with laser-based music systems—just in time for stereo TV broadcasts. This also means you can play prerecorded videocassettes at home and hear the same super "Star Wars" effects you might in the theater.

For those who'd rather create their own movies, there is now a variety of convenient home VCRs that double as portables for recording on the go. Better yet, a new generation of one-piece "camcorders" combines camera, recorder and power source in a single handy package weighing 6 pounds or less. The most recent of these, the 8-mm format adopted by Kodak and Polaroid, differs significantly from the familiar Beta and VHS systems.

To date, the greatest advances in VCR technology have occurred in sound and size. The so-called "hi-fi" VCRs get their name from a change in the way sound is recorded onto videotape, so it helps first to understand how music and pictures are recorded at all.

On a regular audio cassette deck, magnetic tape passes by a stationary recording head at the speed of $1\frac{7}{8}$ inches per second (ips). This speed is adequate for the stationary head to magnetize the tape with a replica of the original audio waveform, which can range from 20 to 20,000 cycles per second (or 20 Hertz to 20 kiloHertz, abbreviated 20 Hz to 20kHz).

Getting the picture

Video signals are a good deal more complex than that, with a frequency range extending out to about 4 megaHertz (4MHz), or 4 million cycles per second. That's 200 times greater than the audio range, and to re-create the waveform accurately, tape would have to move across the recording head 200 times as quickly. Accordingly, 200 times more tape would be required to record the same amount of video.

Instead, video recording is achieved by using a rapidly rotating drum on which the video recording heads (at least two) are mounted. The drum

rotates 30 times per second, effectively increasing the magnetic "writing speed" as the tape moves by slowly (at about 8/10 ips and $1\frac{1}{3}$ ips, respectively, in the fastest Beta and VHS speeds). Additionally, wider tape is used for videocassettes: $\frac{1}{2}$ inch wide compared to 15/100 inch for audio cassettes.

To further maximize the amount of video signal that can be stored on the tape, the tape is twisted around the recording drum at an angle. As a result, video signals appear to be recorded diagonally along the length of the tape, whereas audio signals made with a stationary head run longitudinally along the tape. This so-called helical scan recording results in video writing speeds as high as 270 ips—nine times faster than the best studio open-reel recorders.

That's how a VCR records video signals, but until the advent of the hi-fi Beta and VHS systems, the soundtrack was recorded in the old-time method—by a stationary head located at the very edge of the tape. The problem is that with tape speeds slower than the $1\frac{7}{8}$-ips standard for conventional audio cassettes, sound fidelity is somewhat lacking. Few conventional VCRs can record audio signals much beyond 10kHz, which shortchanges the music's treble content. Meanwhile, the slow speed contributes quite a bit of distortion to the program. Signal-to-noise ratios aren't much better than 45 decibels (dB)—and that's for monaural sound! The ratio drops another 5 dB when the narrow soundtrack is split in two for stereo.

Mono or stereo, these ratios are pretty poor when you consider that the average phonograph record and cassette tape (the latter with Dolby noise reduction) clock in at 60 dB or better (in any signal-to-noise ratio, the higher the dB value, the better). All these ratings suffer further deterioration at slower video recording speeds such as Beta III, or EP (extended play) in VHS. Dolby and other noise reduction systems can clean up a little of the hiss on videotape soundtracks, but even this improvement is confounded by the wow-and-flutter contributed by the slow tape speed—alternately a slurring, then a warbling sound. The final handicap of conventional VCR sound has to do with the tape itself. Because the soundtrack is located at the very edge of the tape, poor tape slitting or any edge-damage caused in shipping or storage will detract from the already sorry quality of sound reproduction.

Let's get helical

The average VCR might be adequate for off-the-air recording of TV soundtracks, but because of its inherent sound impediment, the VCR hasn't been able to match the sonic splendor of videodiscs (especially the laser-read type) in reproducing the music and special effects of movie soundtracks. Until, that is, VCR makers in the Beta and VHS camps devised a way to convert audio to FM signals, and record it helically along with video signals. It's called audio frequency modulation, and you'll sometimes see AFM used as a synonym for Hi-Fi VCRs.

Sony and the other Beta manufacturers were the first to achieve the feat. In Beta Hi-Fi, the stereo audio signal is sandwiched between the luminance (brightness) and chrominance (color) information of the video signal, and deposited on the tape at the same time by the same heads. So the audio soundtrack benefits from the same super-fast writing speed of the helically scanning video heads. The result is a lack of hiss, inaudible distortion and unmeasurable wow-and-flutter.

With a signal-to-noise ratio of 80 dB or better, analog AFM recording approaches digital recording's sound fidelity to the original music. This means the softest sounds don't have to be boosted in order to be heard above tape noise, and the loud signals needn't be toned down to capture their intensity. As an added benefit, AFM recording yields the same results at any tape speed, in both VHS and Beta formats

Depth-multiplexing

The VHS format manufacturers achieve identical results to Beta Hi-Fi, though in a different manner. Instead of shoehorning the frequency-modulated audio between the brightness and color signals, then recording it as a video signal, VHS makers record the audio *beneath* the video information by a process known as depth-multiplexing. VHS Hi-Fi uses two independent audio recording heads mounted on the same drum with the video heads. In rotation, the audio heads precede the video heads and deposit the sound information helically on the deepest layer of the tape. The video heads pass by next and superimpose the color images on the tape's surface.

Both Beta-Hi-Fi and VHS Hi-Fi retain the old stationary audio recording head, to maintain compatibility with older tapes and non-AFM machines. This longitudinal mono or stereo track also can be used for sound overdubs. You can't perform overdubs on the hi-fi Beta or VHS soundtracks, inasmuch as these are recorded between or beneath the video signal.

Just like audio tape decks, most AFM video recorders sport input-level signal controls and measurement meters to help you make a pleasing recording. In addition to video recording and playback, you can use hi-fi VCRs to copy up to five hours (Beta) or eight hours (VHS) of super-high-fidelity music—dubbing, for instance, from laser-read digital audio Compact Discs. The same audio input jacks can be used to record sound from FM radio or stereo TV. Few AFM decks have a built-in *stereo* tuner for TV audio.

Though most hi-fi Beta and VHS video recorders now available are designed as tabletop models for use in the home, some two-piece portables and "convertibles" have appeared. Conventional two-piece portables (composed of separate recorder and tuner-timer components) have been around for some time, but the latest models boast many of the convenience features and special effects as house-bound tabletop units. A recent twist is the convertible—best described as a portable video recorder that docks vertically or horizontally in a chassis that contains TV tuner and program timer. Although some hi-fi VCRs on the market are advertised as portables or convertibles, not all will record AFM stereo when used with a videocamera.

The 8-mm format

Audio Frequency Modulation is part and parcel of the 8-mm camcorder system VCR format.

As its monicker indicates, 8 mm differs from the established Beta and VHS recorder formats in the makeup of its tape cassette. About ⅓ inch wide compared to ½ inch for Beta and VHS, and only slightly larger than an audio cassette. Tape composition (or formulation) is different, too. In order to pack all the video and audio information on a narrower tape, 8 mm uses "pure" metal particle tapes, compared to the metal-oxide formulations employed for most ½-inch tapes. Currently, metal particle cassettes can record up to 120 minutes of video with good, though monaural, FM audio (out to 14kHz).

Although convertible tabletop models are planned by some manufacturers, the 8-mm format currently is represented by camcorders designed for moviemaking on the go. When inserted in special docking decks and connected to a TV, the results can be reviewed. These same decks enable camcorders to record TV off the air, though recording time today is limited to two hours per tape. Adaptors available from the manufacturers also will enable 8-mm camcorder users to dub their recordings onto half-inch tape and thereby

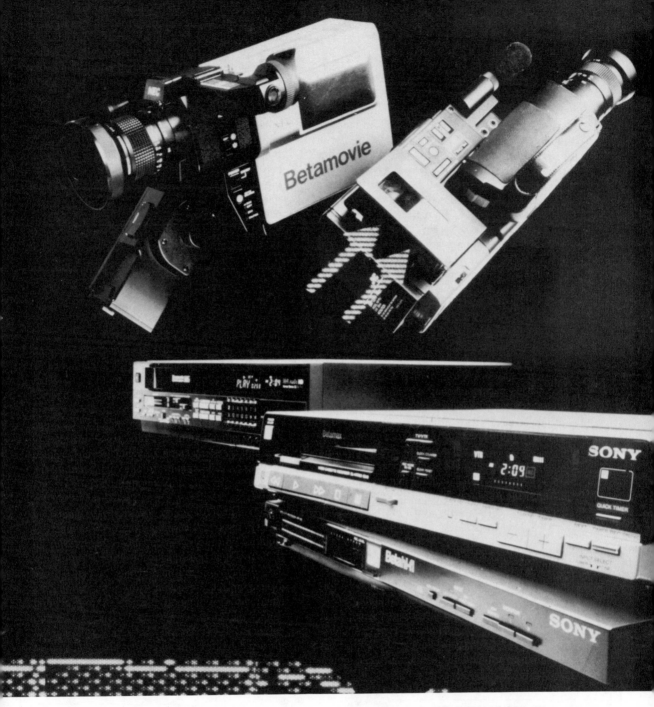

maintain compatibility with their home and portable VCRs.

Like 8 mm, Betamovie and its VHS equivalent, VideoMovie, record at a single speed (the faster Beta II and "SP" modes) but obtain longitudinal, monaural sound on a par with conventional VCRs. The Beta camcorder uses a standard-size Beta cassette permitting up to 3½ hours of moviemaking with an L-830 length tape. VHS VideoMovie employs the compact VHS-C cassette—slightly bigger than 8 mm—for up to 20 minutes of recording time. By inserting the

"TC-20" into a special adaptor, you can review it on a regular VHS recorder connected to a TV. Or, the VideoMovie camcorder can be connected directly to a VHS home deck in order to dub the contents of one or more TC-20 cassettes onto a standard VHS cassette. VHS camcorders that use standard-size cassettes are now under development.

You will notice that up to this point, there's been no mention of technical improvements on the video side of video recorders. In fact, advances in picture quality have pretty much been limited to such special-effects features as freeze-frame, slow-motion and high-speed forward and reverse scan. The stability and clarity of each of these has been improved by the incorporation of extra video heads—as many as five—in the head drum.

VCR picture quality in regular playback and recording remains about where it's been for the past decade. Although the theoretical frequency response of broadcast video signals extends out to about 4MHz, most VCRs pick up and reproduce no more than 3MHz. Because the finer details (or resolution) of an image are found at the highest frequencies, this means a current VCR will produce images somewhat less clearly defined than a good TV broadcast (or a laser videodisc, whose frequency response tops 4MHz).

Another way of describing picture definition is in *lines of horizontal resolution*. This is measured as the number of vertical lines that can be stacked side by side, left to right across your TV screen (and should not be confused with the vertical *scanning rate* of TV—always 525 left-to-right changing lines running from the top to the bottom of your screen). The more lines of horizontal resolution that can be crammed onto a display, the more detailed that display will be. VCRs currently average from 230 to 250 lines. By comparison, high-quality TV monitors can accommodate more than 300. (If you're playing your VCR through a conventional TV, you won't notice the difference.)

Signal-to-noise ratio for most VCRs—that is, the amount of snow you'll see when you play back a tape—is around 40 dB at present. Because the eye is more sensitive to distortion than the ear, a minute 2 dB difference between VCRs will be visible. Manufacturers' printed specifications might not be much help when comparing VCRs, because there are no statutory standards for making measurements. Trust your eyes when shopping, or use comparative tests made by an independent third party that measures all VCR specifications by the same criteria.

According to domestic and foreign manufacturers, there is considerable work in progress to upgrade the visual fidelity of video recorders. Any improvement is likely to come either from the use of high-quality pure metal tape formulations or from the development of low-cost digital processing circuits that will record and reassemble images and colors as a series of numbers—much in the way the laser-digital Compact Disc player handles music.

The consensus among manufacturers places the introduction of these "eye-fi" VCRs some years off—and for good reason. They'll have to be able to play tapes made on current VCRs, so that the memories you record today won't be rendered obsolete by technological progress. When you play those memories back on the VCR of 1995, they might seem fuzzy compared to recordings of more recent vintage. But you'll still be able to recall and enjoy them.

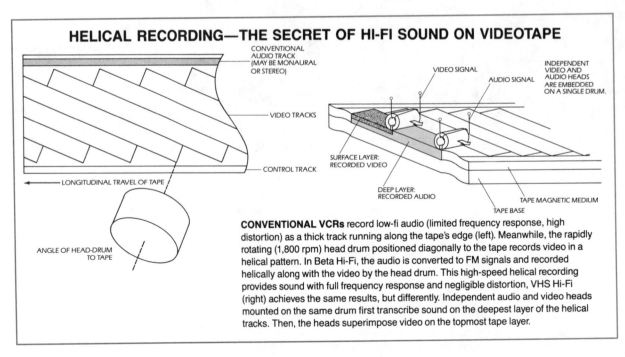

HELICAL RECORDING—THE SECRET OF HI-FI SOUND ON VIDEOTAPE

CONVENTIONAL AUDIO TRACK (MAY BE MONAURAL OR STEREO)

VIDEO TRACKS

CONTROL TRACK

LONGITUDINAL TRAVEL OF TAPE

ANGLE OF HEAD-DRUM TO TAPE

VIDEO SIGNAL

AUDIO SIGNAL

INDEPENDENT VIDEO AND AUDIO HEADS ARE EMBEDDED ON A SINGLE DRUM.

SURFACE LAYER: RECORDED VIDEO

DEEP LAYER: RECORDED AUDIO

TAPE BASE

TAPE MAGNETIC MEDIUM

CONVENTIONAL VCRs record low-fi audio (limited frequency response, high distortion) as a thick track running along the tape's edge (left). Meanwhile, the rapidly rotating (1,800 rpm) head drum positioned diagonally to the tape records video in a helical pattern. In Beta Hi-Fi, the audio is converted to FM signals and recorded helically along with the video by the head drum. This high-speed helical recording provides sound with full frequency response and negligible distortion, VHS Hi-Fi (right) achieves the same results, but differently. Independent audio and video heads mounted on the same drum first transcribe sound on the deepest layer of the helical tracks. Then, the heads superimpose video on the topmost tape layer.

VCR tuneup

■ CLEANING YOUR VIDEOCASSETTE recorder (VCR) entails more than wiping off the top with a dustcloth. To maintain sharp pictures and crisp sound, you sometimes have to get inside and clean the tape mechanism.

What makes a VCR dirty? The principal culprits are the oxide particles that shed from your videotapes and attach themselves to components of the tape transport mechanism. Other factors are airborne dust and household fumes.

Fortunately, videocassettes today don't shed as much as they used to, so cleanups will be few and far between. When should you head for the cleaning tools? When you notice persistently noisy pictures or muffled sound.

Commercially available cleaning cartridges—the kind you use just the way you play a videocassette—do a reasonably good job of removing oxide deposits from the VCR's tape path. In fact, they're all you need if your VCR is the front-loading type.

The construction of front-loaders pretty much seals them off from dust and fumes. Older top-loading VCRs are more vulnerable to airborne contaminants because of their comparatively open design. So, you have to get under the hood occasionally to give your top-loader a good, thorough cleaning.

VCR manufacturers discourage do-it-yourselfers from poking around inside the machine. They feel it's too easy to damage or misalign the delicate video heads—and they're right. If you're careless, you might need a trained repairman to undo your damage.

Because the manufacturers don't want you puttering around in their VCRs, they do not make any technical or servicing information available to the consumer. But if you're a reasonably careful worker, you can perform the simple maintenance

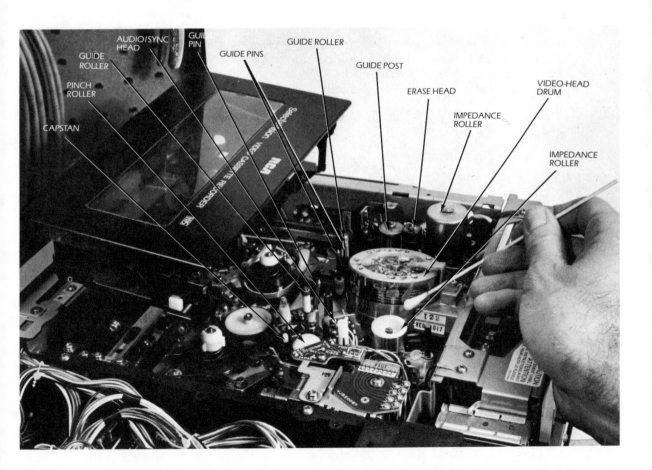

chores outlined here. If you're really serious, you can perform more complex repairs.

You'll find that it's pretty easy to get the cover off the VCR. Typically, there are two or three Phillips-head screws toward the rear of the top and one or two in the back. The case cover should lift off in one piece.

At first glance, the innards of a VCR will baffle you. Whether your VCR is Beta or VHS, you'll find the video head assembly mounted on a large, rotating stainless-steel drum that sits at a crazy angle. There are numerous guide posts—also at odd-looking angles—several guide rollers, roller pins, a capstan which squeezes the tape against a pinch or pressure roller, and two stacks of stationary heads. One contains the erase heads. The other houses the audio and sync-control heads.

All of these components need to be cleaned. We've identified them in the photograph of a typical VHS model. Beta VCRs have the same parts, but their layout is different. Beta or VHS, you should familiarize yourself with the tape travel path by playing a cassette with the VCR's cover off (this is possible on most toploaders). Note the components the tape contacts. These are what you clean—after you've ejected the cassette and unplugged the VCR.

Hard-to-reach dust

Before you clean the tape mechanism, look for accumulated dust in hard-to-reach places. If you've got a mini-vacuum with a small, flexible pickup hose, use it. Otherwise, commercially available canisters of compressed air (used for cleaning cameras) will do.

For actually cleaning your VCR's heads and tape-transport components, get long-stemmed cotton swabs and a bottle of head-cleaner solvent from an electronics store. Bathroom swabs will not reach where you want them to, and will leave globs of cotton on the parts. Also, household rubbing alcohols contain impurities that might cause damage. Don't let the clerk force a demagnetizer on you. Contrary to myth, VCR makers insist demagnetizing is unnecessary with today's video and audio decks. Ditto for lubrication.

Once you've cleared out the loose dust, start swabbing—very carefully. The swab should be damp, not sopping wet. If you saturate the swab, flick off the excess alcohol. Clean the minuscule video heads on the drum with a horizontal motion—not up-and-down.

Rub gently. These heads are delicate, and should never be touched with objects that could scratch them. Similarly, never foul them with a fingerprint. Rotate the cylinder to move the other heads into reachable position by touching the top only. Your VCR might have just two heads on the cylinder or as many as five. Clean them all.

After you've swabbed the video heads, go on to clean the other parts. The order in which you clean doesn't matter, but following the tape path is a good idea. Just be sure to start a fresh swab as soon as you see dirt on the one you're using.

Videotape selection

■ BUYING A VIDEO CASSETTE RE-CORDER might prove to be less confusing than choosing the blank videotape to use with it.

At the very least, most manufacturers offer two grades of tape: standard and high grade. Others offer as many as five. And now, the new wave of hi-fi VCRs has spawned an additional grade of tape, designated "Hi-Fi."

Because pricing among the relative grades can vary from store to store according to discount policies, it's certainly no arbiter of quality. Neither are the brand designations you'll read on the cassette package. Designations such as TDK's Super Avilyn, Fuji's Beridox, Maxell's Epitaxial, Sony's Dynamicron and BASF's Chromium Dioxide are no more than the respective manufacturers' trade names for their proprietary chemical formulation. Current ½-inch (Beta and VHS) formulations always use some form of metal oxide.

'Specs' for the eyes

The lack of technical data on most cassette packages makes direct comparison between brands and grades impossible. Even where the manufacturers provide specifications, they're virtually useless because the comparison relates to that manufacturer's own reference tapes—not to any industry standard.

The only measurements that have any meaning are those reported by independent, third-party tests, which should compare all brands against a common reference. In this case, the important specifications are:

Chroma—the amount of noise or distortion in a color picture, visible as periodic alterations in color shades.

Luminance—the amount of "snow" or noise in a black and white picture, visible as imperfect contrast.

Drop-outs—minute imperfections in the blank tape coating that visibly result in anything from tiny, white spots in a picture to thin, horizontal white lines, and in worst cases, a rolling picture.

Chroma and luminance readings are expressed as "signal-to-noise" ratios (S/N) and are measured in decibels (dB). In each case, the higher

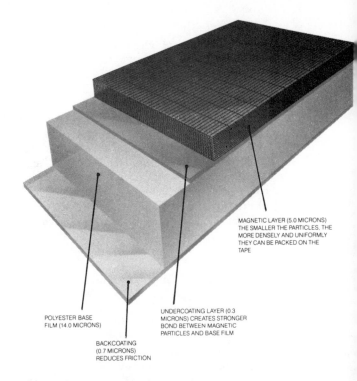

MAGNETIC LAYER (5.0 MICRONS) THE SMALLER THE PARTICLES, THE MORE DENSELY AND UNIFORMLY THEY CAN BE PACKED ON THE TAPE

POLYESTER BASE FILM (14.0 MICRONS)

UNDERCOATING LAYER (0.3 MICRONS) CREATES STRONGER BOND BETWEEN MAGNETIC PARTICLES AND BASE FILM

BACKCOATING (0.7 MICRONS) REDUCES FRICTION

ENLARGED CROSS SECTION shows a typical Beta or VHS super-high-grade videotape. Tapes of this grade add an undercoating and backcoating treatment, which accounts for their higher quality—and higher price. Particle density and antistatic properties are greater, too.

the number the better. Readings of 40 dB for chroma and 44 dB for luminance are average for standard-grade tapes. Drop-outs are measured by their quantity and frequency: A count of 15 drop-outs per minute is average for standard-grade tape. The fewer drop-outs the better. Generally, the higher grades of tape have better measurements. In chroma, for example, a premium tape might register a 3 dB improvement over the standard formulation.

In the absence of third-party test reports, you'll do best to ignore manufacturers' formulation names and rely instead on the grade designation. For both the Beta and VHS formats, there are four general grades: standard, high-grade (sometimes called premium), super-high-grade and hi-fi. However, some companies raise the ante with an ultra-high-grade for the most demanding tasks—usually, recording with a camera.

Ultimately, the best way to determine which tape to buy is a method based upon application. For instance, while most of the new hi-fi grades may work best when used with hi-fi VCRs, they actually vary very little from super-high-grade blank tapes except in one regard: durability.

Why durability?

The importance of durability to a hi-fi tape is illustrated by the way people generally use cassettes. A person recording *Sherlock Holmes Faces Death* may view that movie only three or four times a year.

By contrast, users of hi-fi VCRs generally are music fans, and are likely to view a recording of a video concert as many times as someone else might play the record on a turntable. The tape, therefore, has to be more durable and less drop-out prone, the shell and internal mechanism must be stronger, and better antistatic guards also have to be included. Ultra-high-grades are much the same, but boast better color saturation ability.

Fidelity with economy

Similarly, purchasing by application extends to the other tape grades. High-grade and super-high-grade tapes exhibit their best characteristics when shooting live footage with a video camera. The use of a high-grade tape for your master will provide better quality on any copies you might make. These "dubs" of family events and the like will in turn look best if they're copied onto high-grade tape.

A high-grade tape also is a good investment if you're in the habit of recording at slow speeds to fit three or more movies on a single cassette. Often times, a high-grade or super-high-grade tape recorded at the slowest speed will equal the performance of a standard tape recorded in the faster or normal mode. While the initial price may be higher, the actual cost works out to be lower on a viewing-per-hour basis.

High-grade tapes, it should be noted, offer little meaningful improvement to black-and-white films. Standard tapes will do fine. They also are perfectly suited for time-shifting and most other recording needs at normal speeds, but if you intend to use the same tape each day as your work-horse time-shifting cassette, the investment in a higher grade will pay off in longer tape life.

Tape care tips

The tape grades best suited to your purposes will become apparent after a little experimentation. But the benefits of any tape can easily be lost by improper handling.

Static electricity and dust are the worst enemies of videotape. Static electricity picked up in dry environments or transmitted from carpets quickly attracts dust particles from the air. If dust finds its way onto the tape, the result is an increased drop-out rate, excessive noise and, in severe cases, fouling of the VCR's video heads. To avoid such calamities, always store the tape in its protective sleeve and never leave the cassette in the machine. Dust also adheres to the oils deposited by fingerprints, so never touch the tape itself.

Store on edge

Always store video cassettes on edge and never lying flat. Storing the tape flat puts the weight of the tape pack on the tape's edge, where the audio and control tracks are recorded. Edge damage can destroy a cherished recording. Additionally, storing cassettes on or near items that generate strong magnetic fields (TV sets, loudspeakers) can cause the recording to be erased. Three feet away is a safe distance. If you follow these precautions, your tape library should retain high-fidelity performance indefinitely.

The latest videotape formulations on the street are metal-powder (MP) and metal-evaporated (ME) tapes, used in the new 8-mm camcorders.

Because the 8-mm (⅓-inch) tape is narrower than the ½-inch variety used for Beta and VHS recorders, a more highly magnetic medium is needed to retain sound and images. "Pure," unoxidized metal formulas fill the bill, compared to the metal oxides used for the wider, ½-inch Beta and VHS tapes. Because pure metal particles are more difficult to manufacture and coat, they're two to three times more expensive than the ½-inch oxide formulations.

TWO-HOUR 8-MM TAPE (right) is about the same as 20-minute mini VHS-C tape.

Save slides and movies with your VCR

■ WANT TO DEEP-FREEZE YOUR SLIDES for posterity's sake, but have instant viewing access for yourself? It's easy to put your slides and prints in a "video album" for viewing on your TV. If you've got a videocassette recorder and access to a video camera, all you'll need to get is an accessory called a teleslide converter, or negative-positive adaptor.

These devices attach to your video camera's lens. At the business end is a receptacle for your slides. You simply aim the camera at a light source, focus until the photo's image is clear on your TV screen (or camera viewfinder), then put your VCR into the record mode for the desired length of time. Use the pause button on your camera or VCR when you change slides for a professional cut effect between pictures. If your video camera has a polarity reversal switch (sometimes labeled "positive-negative"), you'll be able to run print negatives through the converter/adaptor and get positive images with natural colors on your videotape.

Besides helping you preserve your photos, transferring to videotape lets you compensate for

A VIDEOCAMERA, VCR and simple inexpensive telecine converter let you transfer 8-mm home movies to videotape. While a converter like this can be easily built in your workshop, finding the right material for the rearprojection screen might be difficult. Plain ground glass may give too much of a hot spot of light to use with your camera.

A TELESLIDE CONVERTER, such as the unit shown here, attaches to a video camera. Slides can be changed like the old-time slide projectors, or the tape paused between slides. You can even add your own soundtrack on the tape. In the background is an adaptor for 8mm camcorders with clips to handle several slides or negatives at once.

photo fading through your video camera's color correction circuits. You can crop photos by using the camera's zoom lens to focus on a specific image in the picture. Or you can position the converter's slide holder so that just a portion of the image is recorded. Finally, trick lenses and filters enable you to add special effects, and you can dub a soundtrack on the tape if you wish.

Convert movies to videotape

You can keep the memories on family movies fresh and sharp by converting your Super-8 and Double-8 film to videotape. Though professional duplicating services can give your family a magnetic new personality, you can do it yourself at home with a minimal investment in equipment.

Unlike film, videotape doesn't grow old and brittle. But preserving those aging, fading celluloid reels isn't the only reason for switching to video. You can store lots of three-minute reels on a single cassette, and you can view them on TV instead of getting out the screens and projectors and threading film with torn sprocket holes. Video also gives you an opportunity to edit your films, add titles, correct colors, dub in a soundtrack (including music) and even indulge in some special effects.

The professional labs use equipment costing as much as $30,000 and capable of the most sophisticated operations. But you can get satisfactory results at home with a simple accessory called a *telecine converter*. We'll assume you have a VCR and TV, and access to a videocamera and film projector.

Use of the telecine converter is fairly straightforward. You aim the film projector into the designated port on one side and focus your vid-

eocamera at the tiny screen on the adjacent side. A right-angle mirror inside the converter reflects the images from your film onto the small rear-projection screen for videotaping. Once you've adjusted both the film projector and the video camera for proper focus, you're ready to roll. Because the videocamera's lens is so close to the telecine converter's super-bright projection screen, the room needn't be dark. You may, however, need a macro lens for your camera if it isn't equipped for close-up shooting.

Keep in mind the importance of synchronizing the film speed to the TV/video system. Double-8 and Super-8 film are shot and projected at the rate of 18 frames per second (fps). The TV/video system used in the United States cans an image 60 times per second. The result of this mismatch is a black bar that will scroll down the images on your TV screen.

Some people don't find the bar objectionable, but it's still best to eliminate it. If your projector has a variable speed control, increase film rate to 20 fps (if the control isn't calibrated, just adjust the speed until the bars disappear). Because 60 is a multiple of 20, you'll be in sync—and without speeding up the action so much that it seems unnatural.

This technique for synchronizing film and video works fine with Double-8 and Super-8 silent film, but creates a complication if there's a soundtrack on your movies. Speeding up the film raises the pitch of the soundtrack, making voices sound funny.

Your VCR and camera enable you to narrate a new soundtrack to replace the old (and usually noisy) one on the Super-8 sound film. But if you really wish to retain the original soundtrack on your film-to-video transfer, there is a way to do it without the voice pitch distortion.

The solution is to use an audiocassette recorder with variable speech control. This audio recorder contains circuits that maintain normal voice pitch even when the tape speed is doubled.

Use the recorder to record the audio portion of your Super-8 at its normal 18 fps speed. Then dub the audiocassette onto your video tape. To sync the voice track to the movie, you should play the audiocassette 11 percent faster than it was recorded.

Because your original soundtrack will probably be very noisy, dub with a good grade of audio tape to avoid adding more noise. The same applies to your video transfer itself. A high-grade or super high-grade videotape will hold up best over time, and make for a good duplicating master.

Home video special effects

■ HOME MOVIES DON'T HAVE TO be boring. Your videocamera production can display some highly creative touches with the application of a few trick effects—the same ones the pros use.

Special effects in video can be electronic or optical. Optical effects are the easier to master, and affordable, too. You can achieve them with readily available filters and lens attachments that fit every videocamera.

There's a wide assortment of special effects available to the videographer. Some of these are already included in your videocamera. Wide-angle, zoom, macro and telephoto lenses are virtually standard features that can be mastered by studying your owner's manual.

Corrective color-balancing also is incorporated in most cameras—so you needn't invest in corrective filters. The special-effects filters you will want to acquire fall into two categories: mild and wild.

Mild enhancement effects are obtained with polarizers, diffusers and graduated color filters. "Trick" or distortion effects are created with multicolor filters, multi-image lenses, starburst and rainbow filters. Try them all and practice, practice, practice until you get the technique down pat. That's the best feature of videocamera work: Tape is inexpensive and can be used over and over again. You're spared the expense of having film developed to learn from your mistakes.

Polarizing filters

One of the oldest enhancement filters is the polarizer, useful for controlling and eliminating unwanted reflections from shiny surfaces. It also cuts down glare on sunny days, as well as atmospheric haze.

Polarizing filters are mounted in holders so that, when rotated, they maximize or minimize the reflections. The effect of the polarizer can be seen either through the filter itself, or through

PHOTO AT LEFT was taken without a filter, the one at right with a polarizing filter. Note how the washed-out effect, caused by reflected light, is brought under control.

THIS THREE-FILTER KIT includes multi-image, rainbow and starburst elements. An adaptor ring might be needed.

your videocamera's viewfinder. Polarizing filters are also highly effective in manipulating sky color without affecting other color tones in a videotaped scene. For example, they'll darken the sky in the background, for dramatic contrast. Using two polarizers mounted in a common revolving-base holder will give more pronounced effects.

For best results, remember that polarizers achieve their maximum blocking effect when the camera is positioned at the same angle to the reflecting surface as the source of light illuminating the surface. To calculate exposure with polarizers, first set the polarizing element in the proper position, then activate the automatic white balance on your video camera. Because polarizers only admit partial planes of light to the camera, exposure increases most likely will be required.

Diffusion filters

Another enhancement filter is the diffusion filter. Diffusion is a means of softening the image, or image sharpness, and can produce some pleasing effects.

The basic (or No. 1) diffusion filter gives a slight soft-focus effect, particularly good in portraits where softness enhances the image while reducing skin blemishes. A No. 2 diffusion filter provides heavier diffusion for an overall dreamlike or fantasy effect. The heaviest of the diffusion filters, called foggilizers, create fog-like effects that can enhance portraits and scenic shots. In spot diffusers, the center is punched out or perforated to allow a soft-focus background while leaving the central image or subject in sharp focus.

With diffusion filters, larger lens apertures will increase the soft focus effect, while smaller apertures serve to minimize or counteract it.

Graduated color filters

Graduated color filters, another enhancement accessory, help compensate for exposure variations in a single picture—for example, a bright sky and dark foreground, or vice versa. They can also create color-enhancement effects: A normal daylight scene can be converted to a sunrise or sunset scene by using pink or violet graduated filters. Always place the color segment of the filter in the area of the image where it will be most effective.

Multicolor filters

Multicolor (bicolor and tricolor) filters are solely for "trick" or exaggerated color effects. When properly applied, they can be visually stimulating. Bicolor filters are half one color, half another. Tricolor filters are composed of three thirds, each a different hue. Multicolor filters are

 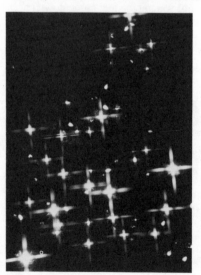

STAR FILTER changes Christmas tree bulbs at left into radiant individual stars. It can dramatically alter the lights of a city taken from a distance.

A MULTI-IMAGE FILTER, as used here, can create hallucinatory effects.

RADIAL-DIFFRACTION FILTERS generate rainbow colors from light sources.

most effective with lighter or brightly lit scenes. The larger the lens aperture used, the more gradual the transition between the color segments.

Multi-image lenses

These "trick" lenses are capable of producing three or more repetitive images on a single video frame. They usually come installed in revolving holders or adapters that allow you to shift or place the multiple images wherever you'd like.

The lenses actually are cut in varying facets. Some lenses that are on the market have prismatic facets that can create up to six multiple-image patterns positioned around a central focal image. Rotating the multi-image lens allows image positioning as desired. Multi-image lenses obtain their best effects with normal focal length lenses.

Starburst filters

Cross-screen filters, better known as "star filters," create an eye-catching star-like effect. By means of an engraved screen surface, the star filter causes the light source to flare out along the grid lines. The stronger and brighter the light source, the more prominent and exaggerated the flaring.

Star filters come in four-point, six-point and eight-point versions. Star filter elements can also be used in combination for added effect. Starbursts are most dramatic when used against black or dark colored backgrounds. They create their most novel effects with night scenes containing point light sources, and with reflecting glassware, jewelry, and incandescent light—especially candlelight. Shooting at large, intense light sources (such as the sun) through star grids is not recommended with tube-pickup cameras because the pickup tube may be damaged seriously. The same recommendation applies to rainbow filters. If your camera uses a solid-state pickup, you're safe.

Rainbow filters

Rainbow filters—or diffraction gratings—break up rays of light to create multicolored flares when aimed at concentrated light sources.

Diffraction filters fall into five general categories. Linear rainbow filters produce repetitive, single-direction light patterns along a straight plane. Radial filters produce flares in spoke-like patterns around a concentrated light source. Circular gratings allow rings of color to surround the light source. Rainbow filters cause a light source to break into surrounding multicolored starbursts; some have a clear center portion for producing softer effects. Nebular gratings create streaked effects, with a splash emanating from the light source and graduating to a circular pattern. More pronounced radical effects may be obtained if the nebula grating is rotated during videotaping.

Diffraction filters produce their predominant effects best when large lens (iris) apertures are used. Overall intensity (thus the "effect") diminishes as the lens is stopped down.

Adding movement

By rotating a rainbow-type filter in its casing, you can impart movement to heighten the imagery of your videocamera production. This is also true of starburst, multi-image and polarizing filters. Although the filters can be rotated by hand, you might find that operation is sporadic and not smoothly controlled when done manually.

One lens-mounted device lets you rotate the inserted filter elements independently of the videocamera's lens. You can rotate the filters continuously or at intervals, in either direction and at variable speeds. A separate, battery-powered unit will allow you to control the movement with one hand.

Contemporary pedestal table

■ YOU'VE SEEN gracefully formed pedestal tables such as this in decorators' magazines, smart boutique shops and fine-furniture store windows. And just as likely, you've gulped at the prices they sell for.

Happily, you can duplicate this table with tools and materials you are probably already familiar with by utilizing a new technique. You can make it for the price of a sheet of plywood, a short piece of pipe and two flanges, a few packages of vinyl patching plaster, paint, some screws and glue.

The sculpting involved is simple, yet challenging and interesting. The technique is a sort of cross between using a potter's wheel and doing clay sculpture—with a little spackling thrown in. The finished piece is graceful, but rugged and

heavy. For a finish, you can paint it white, black or a bright color to suit the room decor. And the same construction techniques can be used to build such items as stands for TV, stereo and the like.

The dimensions for the table shown are entirely arbitrary; the piece was made to be used as a fairly large occasional table. You can make it, of course, any size you wish; in practice, you're limited only by the standard 48-in. width of a plywood sheet.

The basic skeleton of the table is a pair of built-up plywood discs—one for the top, one for the base. The stem is a length of 1½-in. galvanized pipe fastened to the top and the base with pipe flanges and lagscrews. All of the parts are then given shape with a patching plaster. Drill a small hole through the center of each disc to form the pilot-point for penciling the circle. These holes also let you slip a nail through the plywood discs to insure accurate centering when assembling.

To assemble the discs, spread glue evenly on the first disc, center the next smaller size and put a nail in the hole. Drive the 1¼-in. No. 8 screws and move on to the next disc. When all discs assembled, center the two pipe flanges and fasten in place with lagscrews.

You can save time and money by using ordinary plaster of paris for the initial filling. It's best to apply the plaster in two or three coats, starting with a thick mixture and ending with a mixture the consistency of heavy cream. Glob on a trowel-full and screed the shape by holding the

THE PEDESTAL BASE is formed of glued-together plywood discs. Pipe determines the table height.

THE FINAL HEIGHT of the table in the photo (for which a 16-in. pipe was used) is about 24 in. If you decide to increase the table's height, increase pedestal and top circumferences in direct proportion.

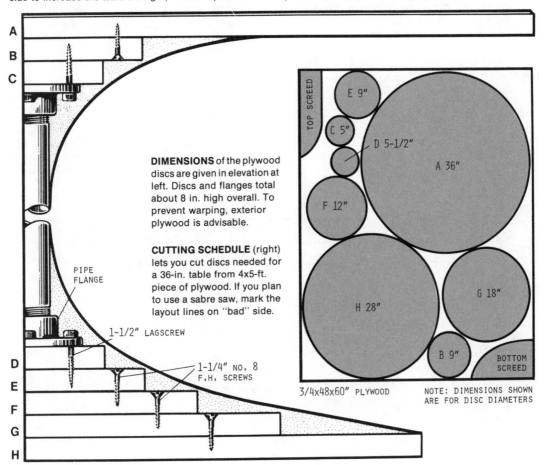

DIMENSIONS of the plywood discs are given in elevation at left. Discs and flanges total about 8 in. high overall. To prevent warping, exterior plywood is advisable.

CUTTING SCHEDULE (right) lets you cut discs needed for a 36-in. table from 4x5-ft. piece of plywood. If you plan to use a sabre saw, mark the layout lines on "bad" side.

PIPE FLANGE

1-1/2" LAGSCREW

1-1/4" NO. 8 F.H. SCREWS

TOP SCREED

E 9"

C 5"

D 5-1/2"

A 36"

F 12"

H 28"

G 18"

B 9"

BOTTOM SCREED

3/4x48x60" PLYWOOD

NOTE: DIMENSIONS SHOWN ARE FOR DISC DIAMETERS

THE FIRST STEP in molding the gracefully curved pedestal is to fill in the "steps" using plaster of paris.

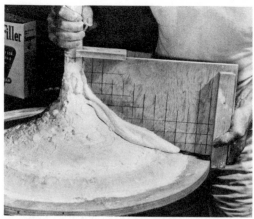

THE FINAL SHAPE is made by screeding patching plaster with a special plywood screed built as shown.

tool (notched block) firmly against the pipe and the cleat against the plywood edge. You'll end up with the shapes quite true, but *not* entirely smooth. Do the final smoothing by laying on joint compound the same way you do when finishing a plasterboard wall.

When the plaster is dry, apply several coats of flat enamel, sanding thoroughly between coats.

If you prefer a durable top for use as a work surface, plastic laminate is a practical choice. In this case, apply a laminate self-edge strip to the plywood edge before laminating the top.

THE SCREED can be cut from scrap plywood lying about the shop. The notched block guides it around the pipe.

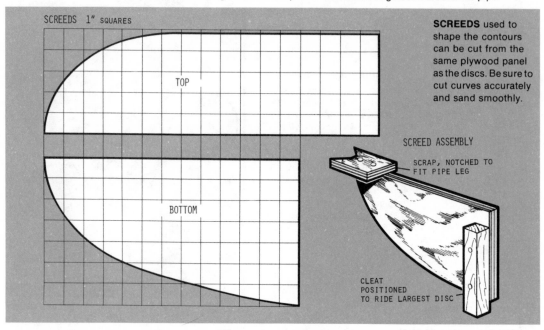

SCREEDS 1" SQUARES

TOP

BOTTOM

SCREEDS used to shape the contours can be cut from the same plywood panel as the discs. Be sure to cut curves accurately and sand smoothly.

SCREED ASSEMBLY

SCRAP, NOTCHED TO FIT PIPE LEG

CLEAT POSITIONED TO RIDE LARGEST DISC

Parsons table

■ BECAUSE OF ITS OVERALL FLUSH DE-SIGN, the Parsons table has always presented a problem to the do-it-yourselfer when it comes to attaching the legs rigidly. You can solve this by making the legs hollow and as an integral part of the whole table. The result is a table with incredibly rigid legs. After you cover all of the exposed surfaces with a decorative laminate, the table appears to be molded of plastic.

The cutting diagram shows how you can economically lay out all 13 parts of the 30x 30x30-in. table on a sheet of 4x8 plywood ¾-in. thick with a minimum of waste. The four U-shape sides are cut alike as are the pieces for the built-up hollow legs. Each side member laps the edge of the adjacent one, which accounts for

one leg of each side being 3 in. wide and the other 2¼ in. All the joints are butted, glued and nailed (or screwed); the top is applied last.

The laminate is applied to the legs first, then to the U-shape sides and finally to the top.

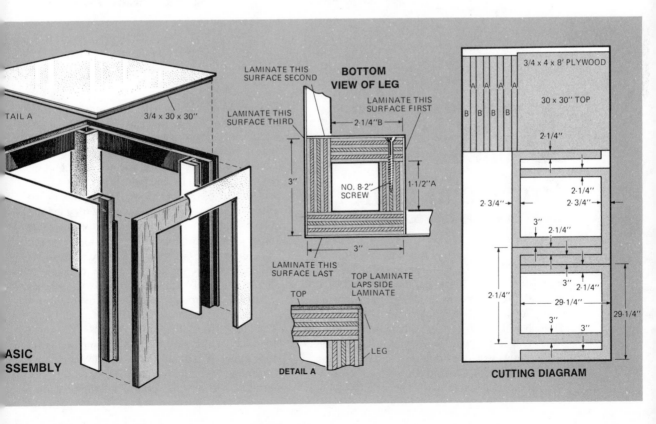

TAIL A   ¾ x 30 x 30″

LAMINATE THIS SURFACE SECOND

LAMINATE THIS SURFACE THIRD

BOTTOM VIEW OF LEG

LAMINATE THIS SURFACE FIRST

2-1/4″B

3″

NO. 8-2″ SCREW

1-1/2″A

3″

LAMINATE THIS SURFACE LAST

TOP LAMINATE LAPS SIDE LAMINATE

TOP

LEG

DETAIL A

ASIC SSEMBLY

¾ x 4 x 8′ PLYWOOD

30 x 30″ TOP

A A A A

B B B B

2-1/4″

2-3/4″

2-1/4″
2-3/4″

3″
2-1/4″

2-1/4″

3″ 2-1/4″

29-1/4″

3″

29-1/4″

3″   3″

CUTTING DIAGRAM

French Provincial table

■ CONSTRUCTED OF cabinet-grade ¾-in. mahogany plywood, this handsome occasional table of French Provincial design can be used singly, or in pairs, in living room or bedroom. Though not a project for a beginning woodworker, it is easier to build than it looks. The design, however, does require the use of some sophisticated shop equipment such as a bandsaw, router and table saw. The original table

shown above is one of a pair; if your need is for a couple of end tables, you can save time by doing all the cutting and assembly for both at the same time.

Begin work by cutting the top and bottom pieces 19½ x 21¼ in. and face three edges with ¾ x 1¾-in. strips of solid stock. These are mitered at the front corners and attached with glue and splines. Then shape the three edges with your router. The grooves in which the doors slide are ¼-in. deep by ½-in. wide. These are made using a router, collars and template. The template is simply a piece of ¾-in. plywood cut to a size that will result in a groove cut in the bottom of the top and the top of the bottom when the router collar is guided around the outer edge. Next, run a blind rabbet along the back to accommodate the back panel. Then cut a slot at a 45° angle and tangent to the back circles. This tangent slot permits insertion of the doors from the back after which the slot is filled in with a small piece.

Make up the two corner posts and the front rail from the pattern given and attach the front rail to the corner posts with dowels or mortise-and-tenon joints, and then secure this subassembly to the front of the bottom by driving screws up through the corner of the plywood and into the end of the corner posts. Next, cut the two 11 x 12½-in. plywood sidepieces and cover the exposed front edges with wood tape. Bandsaw the two side rails, dowel them to the posts and side panels, then drive three 2-in. No. 8 fh screws up through the bottom and into the side panels.

The base is composed of four feet and rails. The feet are bandsawed from blanks of 2⁷⁄₁₆-in.-sq. stock. These can be either laminated or solid blocks. The front and side rails are of stock thick enough to follow the contour of the tops of the legs.

In the original, ⅞-in. mahogany backed up by ¾-in. maple was used. Cut the leg and rail blanks to the correct lengths and mark them for dowels. Notice that the back rail is simply a flat board cut from ¾-in. stock. Take care that the dowel holes are positioned in such a manner that they won't show when the contours of the feet and rails are cut. Bandsaw the four legs and remove excess material from the rails on your table saw. Now assemble the base section. Plane the rails and tops of the feet to match and finish up with a thorough sanding of all members. After attaching the four corner blocks, the completed base should look like that shown.

Now you can make the doors—they make the completed table stand out from run-of-the-mill furniture. With a little extra care along the way, you will be assured of a professional-looking piece of furniture. The slats are of ⁷⁄₁₆-in. mate-

CLAMPS ARE used in gluing the side rails to corner posts and side panels after you glue the front rail.

SLAT DOORS are inserted in track from the rear of the cabinet before the ¼-in. plywood back is installed.

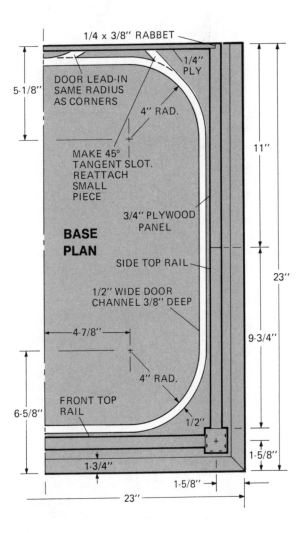

rial; 36 slats are ⅞ in. wide and two—the front ones where the knobs go—are 1¼-in. wide.

Remove the sharp edges from all pieces and sand the front faces only. There's no need to sand the backs of the slats; they're not seen because of the canvas backing. Lay all slats for one door face down on a flat piece of plywood and, using a pipe clamp, clamp them together reasonably tight. Make certain the slats are aligned and square, and clamp the ends down with C-clamps and strips of thick wood.

Cut two 2-in. widths of heavy canvas slightly shorter than the overall length of the clamped-up doors, apply two coats of contact cement to each slat and the canvas strip. When the cement sets, place the canvas strips in contact with the slats and smooth all wrinkles. Keep the assembly in

clamps for at least 20 minutes. *Caution:* When you apply the contact cement to the backs of the slats, do not let any glue run onto the exposed sides (the cement will bleed through the lacquer finish).

When the doors are completed, insert each one in the routed groove or track. Apply a coat of paraffin wax to the bottoms of the slats to ensure sliding ease. It's best to make a dry run of the doors with the top temporarily secured. If necessary, sand slat ends for smooth operation.

It is a good idea to stain the parts before assembly. The original tables were given a coat of sealer and three coats of satin lacquer. However, an antique-white finish with the tambour doors in mauve, makes a handsome piece. Either way, it will be one you will treasure for years to come.

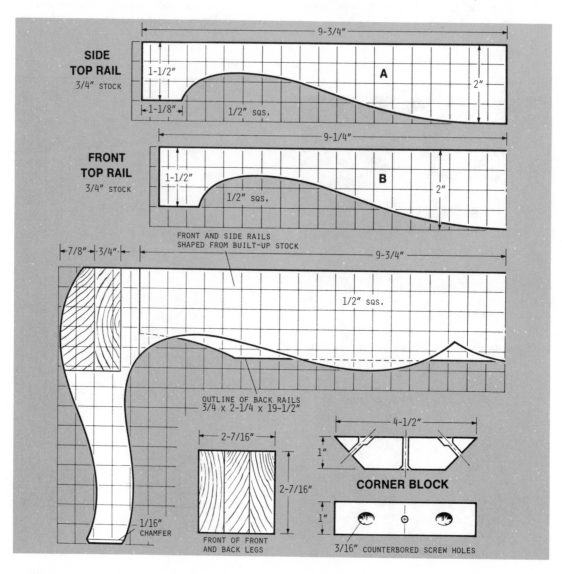

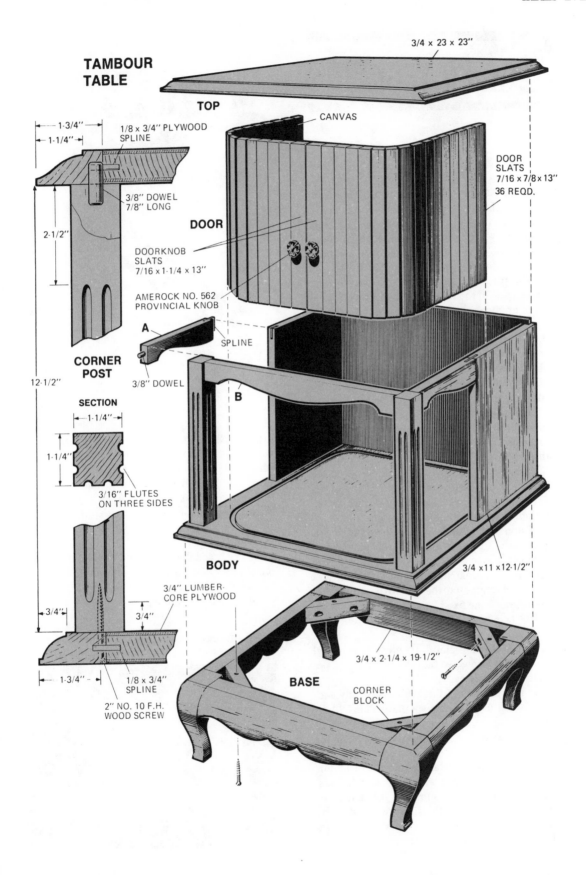

TAMBOUR TABLE

3/4 x 23 x 23''

TOP

CANVAS

DOOR

DOOR SLATS
7/16 x 7/8 x 13''
36 REQD.

1-3/4''

1-1/4''

1/8 x 3/4'' PLYWOOD SPLINE

3/8'' DOWEL 7/8'' LONG

2-1/2''

DOORKNOB SLATS
7/16 x 1-1/4 x 13''

AMEROCK NO. 562 PROVINCIAL KNOB

A

SPLINE

B

3/8'' DOWEL

CORNER POST

12-1/2''

SECTION

1-1/4''

1-1/4''

3/16'' FLUTES ON THREE SIDES

3/4'' LUMBER-CORE PLYWOOD

3/4''

3/4''

BODY

3/4 x 11 x 12-1/2''

1-3/4''

1/8 x 3/4'' SPLINE

2'' NO. 10 F.H. WOOD SCREW

BASE

3/4 x 2-1/4 x 19-1/2''

CORNER BLOCK

Snack table

■ THIS SNACK TABLE folds perfectly flat and only 1¾-in. thick for compact storage. It is made of redwood with a tortoise-shell laminate top, but pine or hardwood and a different style laminate can be used. Along with the plans opposite, here are some additional hints to help you along:

1. The pivot blocks (D) must be attached to the underside of the top (G) with screws and glue prior to applying the plastic laminate. Be sure to countersink the screws.

2. Cut the laminate (H) slightly smaller than the top (G). Apply laminate contact cement to both surfaces to be joined and allow it to dry until it's no longer tacky. Since the laminate will be difficult to move once it is bonded to the top, use kraft paper slipsheets to keep the surfaces apart until they are aligned. Assure a good bond by rapping laminate surface with a hammer on a softwood block.

3. The binding strips can be mitered at the corners, but the joint shown in the plans is less likely to splinter and is also good looking. Attach the binding to G with glue and brads.

4. Since folding tables generally take a beating, be sure all joints are tight. A brad driven through the top of the leg and dowel (E) will help keep this joint from pulling apart. Similarly, a drop of white glue on the tip of the screw that passes through the fixed legs and into pivot block (D) will help prevent it from backing out with use.

5. The aluminum guides (I) must be identical in length and formed so that the swinging legs of the table will slide easily.

Accurate forming of the guides is greatly simplified by the use of jig shown in the plans. Make trial bends on a short piece of aluminum to check for clearance before screwing block (N) to jig permanently.

Then take a short measured length of aluminum strip, say 8-in. long, and form the two ends. Measure the finished length. The difference between the two lengths is the distance that must be added to the length of aluminum strip from which the finished guide will be formed.

6. Finishing the tables is a matter of individual taste. If a hardwood has been used, a rubbed finish with Danish or tung oil topped off with polished hard wax gives a handsome effect.

The aluminum guides can be covered with brass-colored spray lacquer to match brass screws, or with a color that will harmonize with the wood.

All the brads should be set and holes filled with matching wood putty. Use of a hollow-ground saw blade on all cuts will produce surfaces that require only fine sanding.

MAKE TRIAL BENDS on jig before screwing on the block (N); use clamps to secure temporarily.

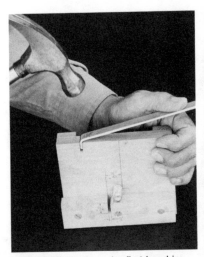

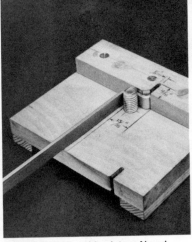

USE EDGE slot to make first bend in guide. Strike strip close to bend.

INSERT BENT end in slot on N and force strip around bolt threads.

MATERIALS LIST—FOLDING TABLE

Key	No.	Size and description (use)
A	4	$3/4 \times 1\frac{1}{8} \times 28\frac{1}{4}''$ redwood (leg)
B	1	$3/4 \times 1\frac{1}{8} \times 14\frac{1}{2}''$ or to fit redwood (brace)
C	1	$1/2''$ dia. $\times 15\frac{7}{8}''$ or to fit dowel (stop)
D	2	$3/4 \times 1\frac{3}{16} \times 2\frac{3}{4}''$ redwood (pivot block)
E	2	$7/16 \times 1/2 \times 20''$ redwood (edging)
F	2	$7/16 \times 1/2 \times 15\frac{1}{2}''$ redwood (edging)
G	1	$3/8 \times 15\frac{1}{2} \times 19\frac{1}{2}''$ plywood or particle board (top)
H	1	$1/32 \times 15\frac{1}{2} \times 19\frac{1}{2}''$ plastic laminate
I	2	$1/8 \times 1/2 \times 18''$ cut to suit aluminum (guide)
J	2	$1\frac{1}{2}''$ No. 10 fh brass screw
K	11	$1\frac{1}{4}''$ No. 10 fh brass screw
L	4	$1/2''$ No. 10 pan head screw
M	1	$3/4 \times 5 \times 6''$ hardwood (bending jig)
N	1	$3/4 \times 1\frac{1}{2} \times 6''$ hardwood (bending jig)
O	2	$1/2 \times 3/4 \times 6''$ hardwood (bending jig)
P	1	$1/2''$ dia. $\times 1\frac{1}{2}''$ hex bolt (bending jig)

Misc. $3/4''$ brads, glue, and laminate contact cement as you require.

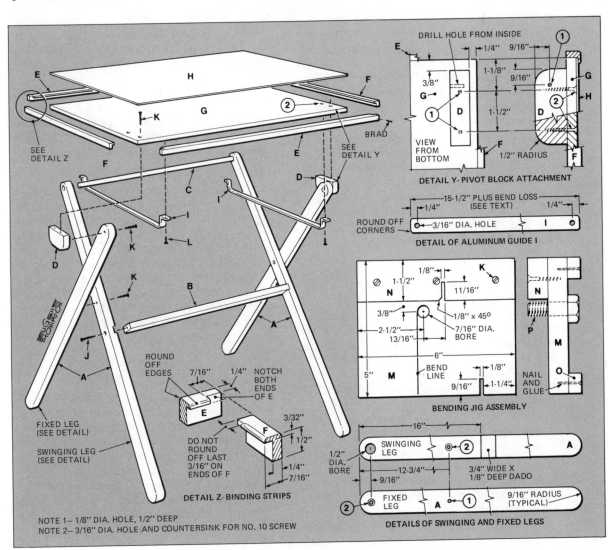

DRILL HOLE FROM INSIDE

3/8"
G
1/4" 9/16"
1-1/8"
9/16"
1-1/2"

VIEW FROM BOTTOM

1/2" RADIUS

DETAIL Y- PIVOT BLOCK ATTACHMENT

15-1/2" PLUS BEND LOSS (SEE TEXT)
1/4"
ROUND OFF CORNERS
3/16" DIA. HOLE
1/4"

DETAIL OF ALUMINUM GUIDE I

1/8"
1-1/2"
N
3/8"
2-1/2"
13/16"
7/16" DIA. BORE
1/8" x 45°
11/16"
K
6"
BEND LINE
5"
M
9/16"
1-1/8"
1-1/4"
P
NAIL AND GLUE

BENDING JIG ASSEMBLY

16"
SWINGING LEG
1/2" DIA. BORE
12-3/4"
9/16"
3/4" WIDE X 1/8" DEEP DADO
A
FIXED LEG
A
9/16" RADIUS (TYPICAL)

DETAILS OF SWINGING AND FIXED LEGS

SEE DETAIL Z
SEE DETAIL Y
BRAD
DRILL HOLE FROM INSIDE

ROUND OFF EDGES
7/16" 1/4" NOTCH BOTH ENDS OF E
E
DO NOT ROUND OFF LAST 3/16" ON ENDS OF F
F
3/32"
1/2"
1/4"
7/16"

DETAIL Z- BINDING STRIPS

FIXED LEG (SEE DETAIL)
SWINGING LEG (SEE DETAIL)

NOTE 1— 1/8" DIA. HOLE, 1/2" DEEP
NOTE 2— 3/16" DIA. HOLE AND COUNTERSINK FOR NO. 10 SCREW

Nesting party tables

■ WHEN IT COMES to storing, these individual serving tables are no problem. They all nest neatly within a lamp table to become part of it.

You'll find them handy whenever a small chairside table is needed to hold a drink, ashtray or sandwich. They're perfect, of course, for a children's party.

The best way to wind up with four identical nesting tables is to mass-produce them. For example, the four top shelves can be bandsawed at one time, likewise the four center shelves and the four bottom shelves. Stock for the eight backs can be ripped $11^{13}/_{16}$ in. wide, then cross-cut into $19\frac{1}{2}$-in. lengths. Stock for the fluted aprons is grooved, kerfed on the back and then ripped crosswise into four strips 2 in. wide.

Run the miters on the eight backs before you cut back the front edges. To cut the latter, run your table-saw blade as high as it will go and set the fence for a ¾-in. cut. Then rip four of the backs for a distance of 8 in. Do the same with the other four after resetting the fence to the left side of the blade. This will produce four right and four left-hand members. Finish the cuts by sawing in from the edge on a ¾-in. radius, then round off the top corner.

Cover with laminate

The tops and front edges of all 12 shelves are covered with decorative laminate in whatever color you prefer. The edges are banded first, then the surfaces, except the four top shelves. Wait until these shelves are nailed in place.

You can save a lot of masking if you paint the inside surfaces of the backs before installing the shelves. Glue and nail the mitered edges, keeping the assemblies square, sink and putty the nailheads and spray with two coats of white semigloss lacquer.

Any void found in the plywood at the front edges should be puttied beforehand, of course, and sanded smooth. The center and bottom shelves are nailed in place from the back, while the top shelves are nailed down from the top.

Making the flutes

This leaves the fluted aprons. Two pieces of ¾-in. pine, 8¼ in. wide, are edge-glued to make a board 16½ in. wide. Notice that the grain must run vertically. Twenty-two flutes are made across the board, either with a ¾-in. core-box router bit or a molding head on your table saw. If you make them on your saw, use a ¾-in. scrap for a spacer. Set the fence to make the first cove and make the cut. Then with the work brought back against the fence and held intact, back the fence away and drop in the ¾-in. scrap. This is done each time as you work across the board. The last cove cut should arrive at the very edge of the board.

Now a series of ½-in.-deep, closely-spaced saw cuts (kerfs) is made on the back of the board, with the grain, and completely across its width, after which the board is ripped crosswise into 2-in.-wide strips. The kerfing permits bending the strips so they can be glued to the curved cleats which are screwed to the underside of the bottom shelves. Notice that the cleats are set in ⅞ in. from the front edge. You can now complete painting to suit your taste.

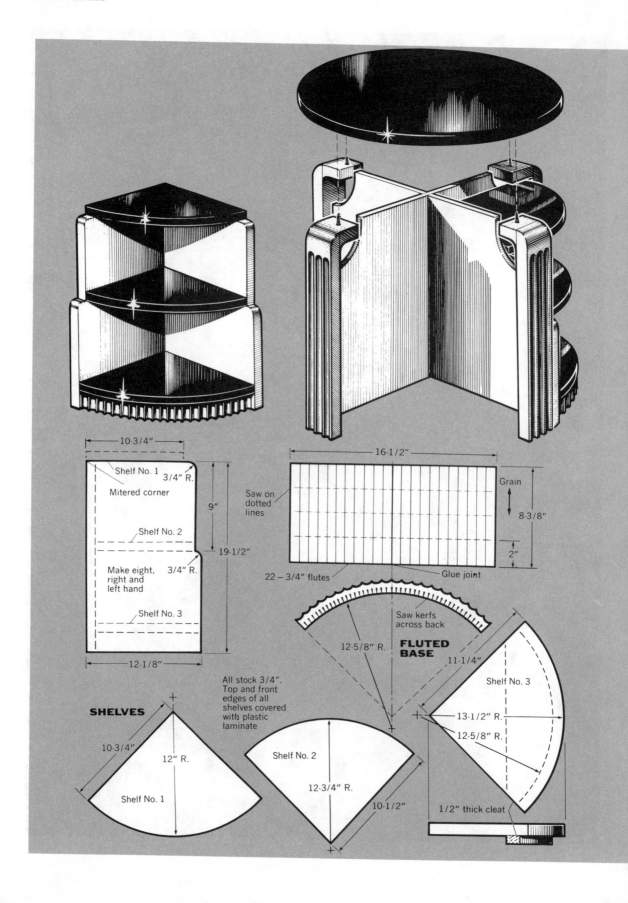

10-3/4"

Shelf No. 1
3/4" R.
Mitered corner

9"

Shelf No. 2

19-1/2"

Make eight,
right and
left hand
3/4" R.

Shelf No. 3

12-1/8"

16-1/2"

Saw on
dotted
lines

Grain

8-3/8"

2"

22 — 3/4" flutes

Glue joint

Saw kerfs
across back

12-5/8" R.

**FLUTED
BASE**

11-1/4"

Shelf No. 3

13-1/2" R.

12-5/8" R.

All stock 3/4".
Top and front
edges of all
shelves covered
with plastic
laminate

SHELVES

10-3/4"

12" R.

Shelf No. 1

Shelf No. 2

12-3/4" R.

10-1/2"

1/2" thick cleat

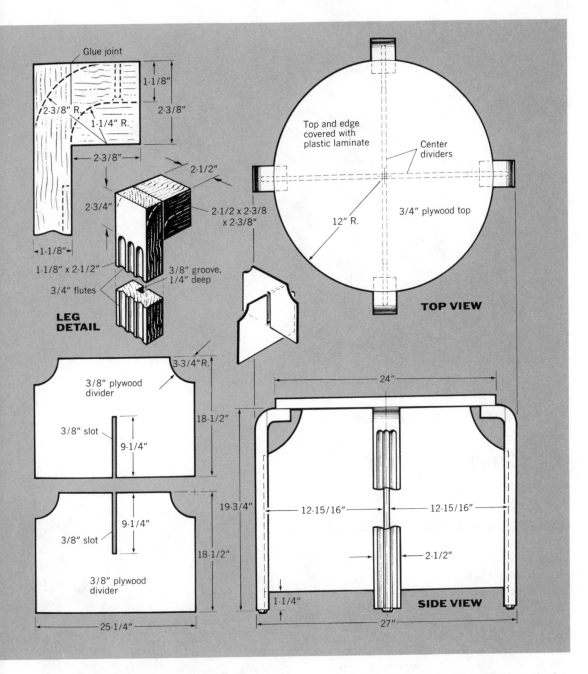

Glue joint

1-1/8"
2-3/8"
2-3/8" R.
1-1/4" R.
2-3/8"
2-1/2"
2-3/4"
2-1/2 x 2-3/8 x 2-3/8"
1-1/8"
1-1/8" x 2-1/2"
3/4" flutes
3/8" groove, 1/4" deep

LEG DETAIL

Top and edge covered with plastic laminate
Center dividers
3/4" plywood top
12" R.
TOP VIEW

3-3/4" R.
3/8" plywood divider
3/8" slot
9-1/4"
18-1/2"
9-1/4"
3/8" slot
3/8" plywood divider
19-3/4"
18-1/2"
25-1/4"

24"
12-15/16"
12-15/16"
2-1/2"
1-1/4"
27"
SIDE VIEW

To build the circular parent table, start with the legs. These are cut to size from 1⅛-in.-thick pine and grooved down the center on the inside for a distance of 16 in. to accommodate the two plywood dividers. Blocks are then glued to the upper ends of the legs, scribed with a compass, bandsawed and sanded. Three ¾-in. flutes are run in the face of all four legs and stopped 2¾ in. from the top. Then holes are drilled for flatheaded screws for attaching the legs to the circular top.

The dividers are made alike except one is slotted down from the top. Add a little glue to the slots and slide them together, then add glue to the grooves in the legs and insert the dividers. They should be flush with the tops of the legs.

This leaves the circular top which is cut from ¾-in. plywood and covered with matching decorative laminate. Complete the painting before attaching the top, and finally hammer metal furniture glides into the ends of the legs. Your tables are ready for use.

Stacking tray tables

■ THIS HANDSOME serving table will prove to be a conversation piece at a party as well as a very functional piece of furniture when it comes time for snacks. Five good-sized triangular tables store conveniently to add to the striking design, as do the legs, which are contained along the sides of the table. The construction is sturdy—¾-in. plywood surfaced with flexible plastic laminate in a smart white, leather-textured pattern.

The legs are simply 1-in. dowels cut to length and sanded smooth. Sixteen dowels are used in the interest of symmetry; only 15 are required for the 5 tables. The tables are set up by simply inserting three legs borrowed from the main table.

Make the brackets for the legs by drilling three 1-in.-dia. holes at a 65° angle in triangles of plywood and glue them to the underside of the

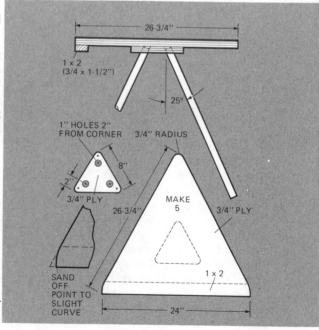

tables in the center. Add five pairs of cleats to the inside and three swivel casters on the bottom.

Use a plywood blade to cut the five triangular tabletops to minimize sanding of the side edges, which will be left exposed and simply painted. Double up the table fronts by adding ¾ x 1½-in. strips after jointing the front edges smooth. Cut the laminate (with knife or scratch awl) about ¼ in. oversize. Apply contact cement to both surfaces; apply the laminate.

The top and base of the main table are built up to double thickness around the edges to provide a "thick look." You can rough-cut the top and bottom panels, glue on the extra strips, and then cut to the required dimensions. A bandsaw is best for this, but you can do it with a sabre saw. In either case, the edges must be trued up with a stationary disc or belt sander. Since the edges are curved, it will be easier to apply the edge trim in two or even three sections, rather than work with one continuous strip.

After the edge trim is applied to the top and base, proceed to add the laminate to the outer portions of the base top surface. Do *not* laminate the tabletop until after the unit is completely assembled. Mark off the positions of the dowel holes and bore small pilot holes through both base and top at the same time to guarantee alignment. Then bore 1⅛-in. holes for the dowels; ⅝ in. deep in the base, and all the way

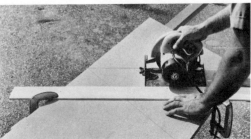

CLAMP GUIDE to work and use a smooth-cutting plywood blade. You can get two tops from a 2x4-ft. panel.

LAY OUT triangular patterns on laminate; allow at least ¼ in. waste all around for final trimming.

WHILE LAMINATE is tough, it can be cut with a utility knife or scored with an awl and snapped off.

APPLY CONTACT cement with notched spreader, let set 30 minutes. Tap laminate with a block for good bond.

FINISH OFF the edges with a router and a bevel cutter set for very slight cut. (Can also be done with file.)

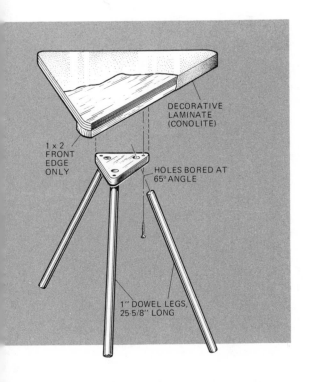

DECORATIVE LAMINATE (CONOLITE)

1 x 2 FRONT EDGE ONLY

HOLES BORED AT 65° ANGLE

1" DOWEL LEGS, 25-5/8" LONG

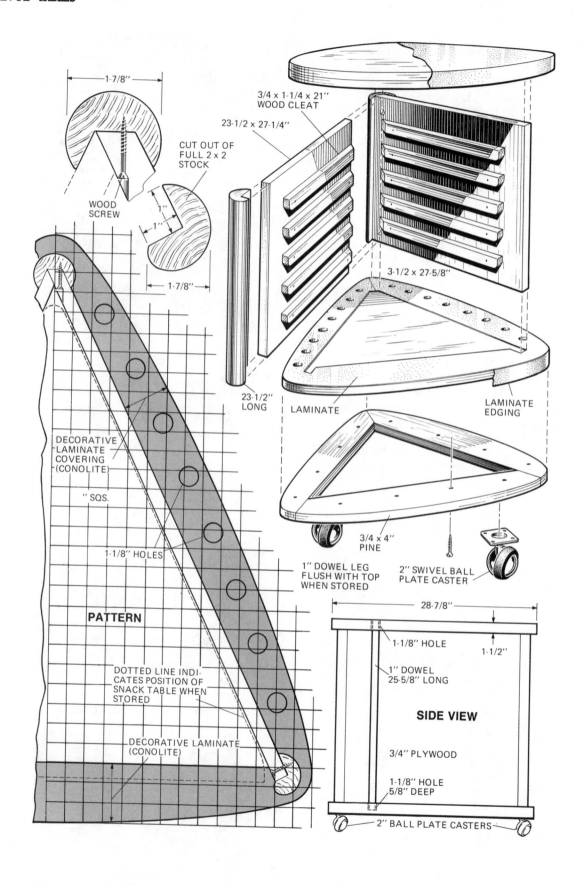

1-7/8''

CUT OUT OF
FULL 2 x 2
STOCK

WOOD
SCREW

1''

1''

1-7/8''

3/4 x 1-1/4 x 21''
WOOD CLEAT

23-1/2 x 27-1/4''

3-1/2 x 27-5/8''

23-1/2''
LONG

LAMINATE

LAMINATE
EDGING

DECORATIVE
LAMINATE
COVERING
(CONOLITE)

'' SQS.

1-1/8'' HOLES

PATTERN

DOTTED LINE INDI-
CATES POSITION OF
SNACK TABLE WHEN
STORED

DECORATIVE LAMINATE
(CONOLITE)

3/4 x 4''
PINE

1'' DOWEL LEG
FLUSH WITH TOP
WHEN STORED

2'' SWIVEL BALL
PLATE CASTER

28-7/8''

1-1/8'' HOLE

1-1/2''

1'' DOWEL
25-5/8'' LONG

SIDE VIEW

3/4'' PLYWOOD

1-1/8'' HOLE
5/8'' DEEP

2'' BALL PLATE CASTERS

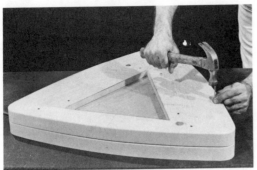

MARK OFF and drill pilot holes through top and bottom at the same time to align dowel holes in the base.

SUPPORT THE HEAVY pieces on drill press for a neat drilling job. Holes in the base are only ⅝ in. deep.

HOLD OFF laminating plywood top until it's glued and nailed to the sides with 2½-in. finishing nails.

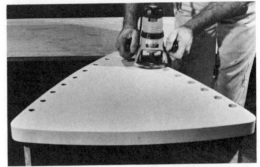

BORE UNDERSIZE holes in plastic covering 1-in. holes, then rout to conform to the diameter of holes below.

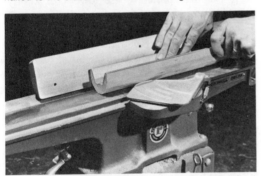

FORM THE TRIM pieces on the jointer, being careful not to trim fingers. Complete shaping with a sander.

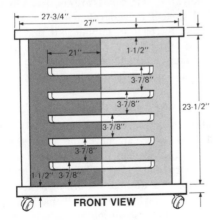

FRONT VIEW

27-3/4"
27"
21"
1-1/2"
3-7/8"
3-7/8"
3-7/8"
3-7/8"
23-1/2"
1-1/2" 3-7/8"

through the top. Add the laminate to the side panels.

The reason the plastic is not applied to the top until after final assembly is to permit nailing the top into the sides. Use glue and 2-in. finishing nails. Although the dowel holes are already bored in the top panel, the laminate is applied in a solid piece without attempting to predrill and align the holes. When the top is laminated, simply bore holes just large enough to allow the router bit to penetrate; then rout them to size.

Make the vertical wood trim for the front and back corners by first doing the required inside cuts, followed by a few angled cuts on the table saw. You can further shape them close to size on the jointer by continually changing the angle of the fence. But watch your fingers.

Some tips on painting: Tack lengths of wire to the bottoms of the dowels and hang them on a line for easy spraying semigloss black. Give edges of individual tables a coat of wood sealer before you paint them with a brushing lacquer.

WEAR SAFETY GOGGLES

Early American hutch table

■ WHEN A CHAIR-TABLE has storage area below the top, it is usually called a hutch-table. Technically, according to the antique experts, it should be called a trestle table.

This hutch-table design has been extremely popular and it is fairly easy to build. With a little time, any average home craftsman can create a beautiful piece of furniture for a living room or dining room.

Besides its charm, a hutch-table is particularly practical. When it's not needed as a table, you can position it against a wall to serve as a decorator piece fitted with a lamp or seat cushion.

Table serves many uses

Our experience has proven this table to be one of the most practical—and treasured—pieces in our home. Since it is so easy to flip down the "back" to create a table, it is frequently used for buffet parties or whenever the kids have a gang in on a rainy afternoon. Because it is constructed in the primitive Early American style—distressed and antiqued—the table looks as good as, if not better than, it did new. Aging has just added to the patina of the wood, and nicks and scratches have simply been filled with a quality stain-concealer. Even if it has had some wear, it can be refinished and look good again.

Selecting materials

For best results, use either Idaho, eastern or sugar pine to make the table. However, if you have the desire, and confidence in your cabinetry skills, there's no reason not to make it of cherry, walnut or any other fine hardwood. For economy, you may prefer to use lower-cost knotty pine. This could be a mistake over the long pull because the material is more frustrating to work with, and stands a better-than-average chance of checking and splitting over a period of time in a heated home. But if you do select such material, lay out the various parts carefully. Do not have knots fall along a line where cutting and shaping will occur. When you're rounding those corners, there's a strong possibility the knots will fall out entirely.

Edge-gluing

Because of the width of the bench sides, top and shelves (E), these parts are cut from glued-up stock. Use stock no wider than 4 in. to avoid any chance of warpage or cupping—if that were to happen to the cabinet, it could stop the drawers from sliding. Professionals alternate the annular rings of the boards being edge-glued as shown.

Edges must be square

Edges to be joined must be perfectly square. If desired, you can have the boards pushed through a planer at your lumberyard for a slight charge. Use glue and dowels to make up the boards to desired width; then clamp the boards, but don't overtighten them. Simply run the clamps to close all joints neatly. Sight along

CHARM AND FUNCTION are the distinctive features of this hutch-table. When the table is not in use (left), the hutch is provided with a cushion for an extra seat. The other photos show the practical unit in service for functional table needs.

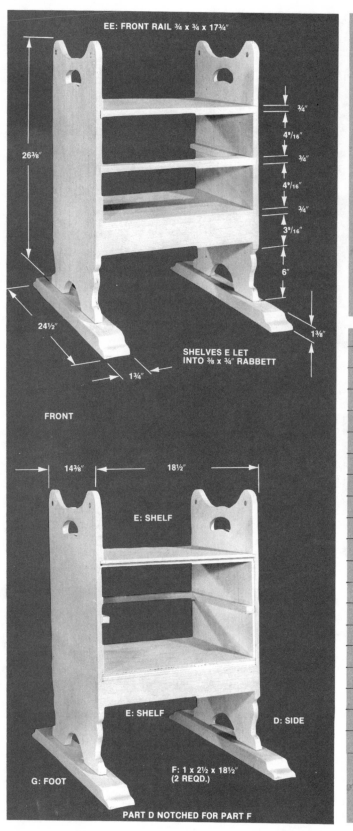

EE: FRONT RAIL ¾ x ¾ x 17¾"

26⅜"

¾"
4⁵/₁₆"
¾"
4⁵/₁₆"
¾"
3⁵/₁₆"
6"
1⅜"

24½"

1¾"

SHELVES E LET INTO ⅜ x ¾" RABBETT

FRONT

14⅜"   18½"

E: SHELF

E: SHELF   **D: SIDE**

G: FOOT

**F: 1 x 2½ x 18½"
(2 REQD.)**

PART D NOTCHED FOR PART F

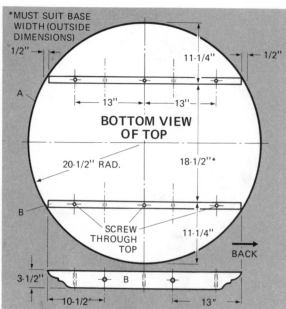

*MUST SUIT BASE WIDTH (OUTSIDE DIMENSIONS)

1/2"   11-1/4"   1/2"

A

13"   13"

BOTTOM VIEW OF TOP

20-1/2" RAD.   18-1/2"*

B

11-1/4"

SCREW THROUGH TOP

BACK

3-1/2"   B

10-1/2"   13"

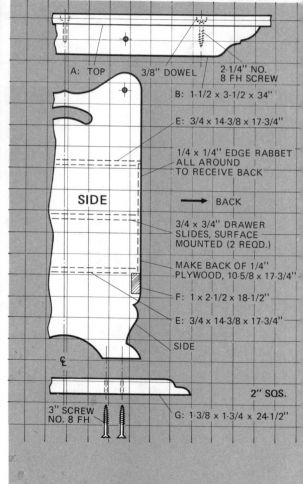

A: TOP   3/8" DOWEL   2-1/4" NO. 8 FH SCREW

B: 1-1/2 x 3-1/2 x 34"

E: 3/4 x 14-3/8 x 17-3/4"

1/4 x 1/4" EDGE RABBET ALL AROUND TO RECEIVE BACK

SIDE   BACK

3/4 x 3/4" DRAWER SLIDES, SURFACE MOUNTED (2 REQD.)

MAKE BACK OF 1/4" PLYWOOD, 10-5/8 x 17-3/4"

F: 1 x 2-1/2 x 18-1/2"

E: 3/4 x 14-3/8 x 17-3/4"

SIDE

2" SQS.

3" SCREW NO. 8 FH   G: 1-3/8 x 1-3/4 x 24-1/2"

the edge to make certain you haven't "clamped in" a warp. When satisfied with the setup, wipe off all excess glue and set the section aside to dry for at least 24 hours. Follow the same procedure for all edge-glued members.

While these parts are drying, use the patterns shown on 2-in. squares to lay out the curved members: feet and top braces. These are best cut by a band saw and next-best cut by a sabre saw with a long blade. You can, of course, do the shaping with a coping saw; it will just take longer. After cutting, sand the shaped portions until smooth and rounded.

Cut both sides together

The next day, you can lay out the sides and top and cut to shape. Important: Temporarily tack the sides together and cut both at the same time. Then, lay out the locations for the dadoes for the top and bottom shelves (E) and push the pieces through the dado-head cutters. To prevent any chance of the piece drifting as you cut the dadoes, use your miter-gauge clamping device. There's no need to dado the sides for the drawer slides. These are simply surface-mounted ¾-in. square strips of hardwood.

With all parts cut and sanded, temporarily assemble the piece and mark the back (side and shelves) for rabbeting for the plywood back panel. Disassemble the piece and, using your router and a ¼-in. rabbet cutter, make the edge rabbet. Then chuck a ¼-in. rounding-over (¼ round) bit in the router and round all edges including top and bottom edges of the top. You will not be able to use the router to round over the shaped edges of the ends of the feet. Use a Surform file and round file. Finally, sand all pieces, working up to a fine-grit paper.

Locating the top

Lay the top good-side down on your workbench. Turn the bench upside down and center it on the top. *Note: For strength, braces should be perpendicular to direction of boards in the top.* When you're satisfied with the fit, position the braces along the outside of the cabinet, leaving some tolerance (about ¹⁄₁₆ in. on each side). Next, mark the brace locations and remove the bench. Making certain that the braces stay aligned with your pencil marks, tack the braces in place using 4d finishing nails through the ends of the braces. Flop the top and use a long straight-edge to draw a line directly over the center of the braces. Drill and counterbore three holes for each brace as indicated in the drawing. Turn in the screws and,

after applying glue, push in short lengths of dowel plugs. (Good doweling technique calls for leaving dowel plugs slightly above the surrounding surface. When glue has dried, the protruding dowels can be sanded flush with the top.)

Hinge pins are simple affairs. All four are made alike, each from two parts, a 3-in. block of pine and a 4¼-in. length of ½-in. dowel. It's easier to make these production style, cutting all blocks at the same time. Ditto the dowel cutting, chamfering, drilling and sanding steps. Dowels are simply glued in the blocks.

To locate the holes in bench sides and braces (part B), set the bench right-side up on your workbench. Position the tabletop on the bench. Note there is a difference in spacing of holes— you need greater distance at the back where the top will pivot. When the top is lined up, use two C-clamps on the ends of one brace to lock the top securely to the bench side. You'll need a ¹⁄₁₆-in. shim to maintain that clearance mentioned earlier. If you're right on, a scrap of laminate is just the thing for a perfect shim.

Carefully bore holes in sides

With a ½-in. spade bit, bore the holes through the first brace using a backup board on the side to prevent splintering when the bit breaks through. Then, leaving the clamps in place, swing around to the other side and bore the pair of holes required there. Remove the clamps and test-fit the hinge pins. They should fit snugly and not slide freely. If they are too tight, enlarge the holes slightly with a round file. Later, when the table is completed, you can always spray on silicone so that the pins will slip in and out of place without fracturing.

Drawers are of standard construction. The fronts are of ¾-in. stock; sides and back of ½-in. stock and the bottom of ¼-in. plywood. The front and sides are dadoed (½ in. up from the bottom edge) to receive the drawer bottom. And the sides are let into an edge-rabbet on the drawer front. Notice that the drawer back is cut narrower than the sides. This method simplifies construction; the back simply fits into edge-rabbets on the sides, and the bottom is attached by driving brads up through the bottom into the back. Lay out for the drawer knobs and drill these holes to suit the knob screws.

Finishing the piece

When satisfied that the piece is sanded smooth, give it a thorough dusting. Next, apply a honey-tone pine stain and after 10 to 15 minutes, de-

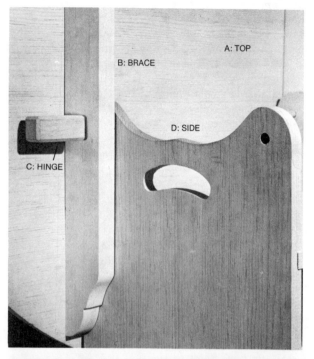

A: TOP

B: BRACE

D: SIDE

C: HINGE

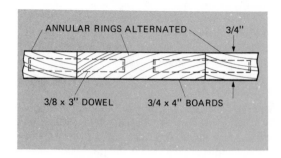

ANNULAR RINGS ALTERNATED   3/4"

3/8 x 3" DOWEL   3/4 x 4" BOARDS

pending upon desired shade-depth, wipe off the excess stain and allow the piece to dry overnight. Apply a wash-coat of shellac to seal the wood and allow to dry.

Apply at least two coats of satin varnish at least 24 hours apart and buff lightly with 00-grade steel wool between coats. Let the piece cure for four to six weeks; after that, if desired, it can be rubbed with paste wax.

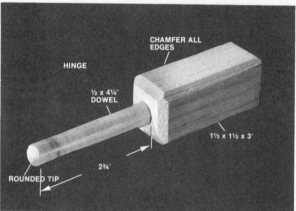

CHAMFER ALL EDGES

HINGE

½ x 4¼" DOWEL

1½ x 1½ x 3"

ROUNDED TIP

2¾"

TABLETOP PIVOTS on pair of "hinges" (upper left). When top is down, second pair is used at front to securely lock the top in place. The required four hinge-pins are constructed alike (middle). All pins (dowels) should fit snugly in holes in braces and sides. Drawer construction is basic (lower left); bottom is let-into sides and front. To affix back, use 4d finishing nails up through bottom. In the diagram above, narrow boards are edge-glued and doweled to make up pieces for sides, shelves (E) and top. To lessen chance of warpage, annular rings should be alternated.

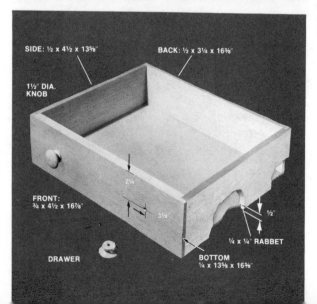

SIDE: ½ x 4½ x 13⅝"   BACK: ½ x 3¼ x 16⅜"

1½" DIA. KNOB

2¼"

FRONT: ¾ x 4½ x 16⅞"

3½"

½"

¼ x ¼" RABBET

DRAWER

BOTTOM ¼ x 13⅝ x 16⅜"

Hutch table of solid pine

■ THE HUTCH table has so many attractive design features that if it hadn't been developed in Europe in the 1600s (and brought to the United States in the early 1700s) it would have been invented here. No other piece of furniture is quite as versatile.

Begin building the table by edge-joining enough stock for both table sides. Use glue and

⅜-in.-diameter dowels, and clamp both assemblies overnight.

Next, lay out the arcs on each side by drawing a series of circles with a compass and pencil, starting with a 5-in.-radius circle along the bottom edge.

Move to the top side corners and draw the 2-in.-radius circles shown on the drawing. (This is also a good time to locate the center points for the hinge peg holes. Measure down 2½-in. from the side's top edge and 1½-in. in from the side edge and mark the intersection. Do this for both corners, then bore 1/16-in.-diameter holes through these points. Do not enlarge the holes yet.)

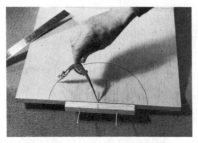

1 LAY OUT arc on bottom of each side. Because circle's centerpoint falls on edge, add a block.

2 MAKE CUT with sabre saw and pivot guide. Apply tape to cut line and support waste with clamp.

3 TOP OF SIDE has three arcs. Draw outside ones first, then middle one. Connect them with tangent lines.

4 TO AVOID sanding out pencil marks, apply tape to stringer and top, mark screw locations on tape.

5 PREBORE holes in leg wing, then cut arc with hole saw. Block clamped to wing provides center.

6 TO MAKE hinge pegs, bore dowel holes in larger dowel and wooden door pull, then join with small dowel.

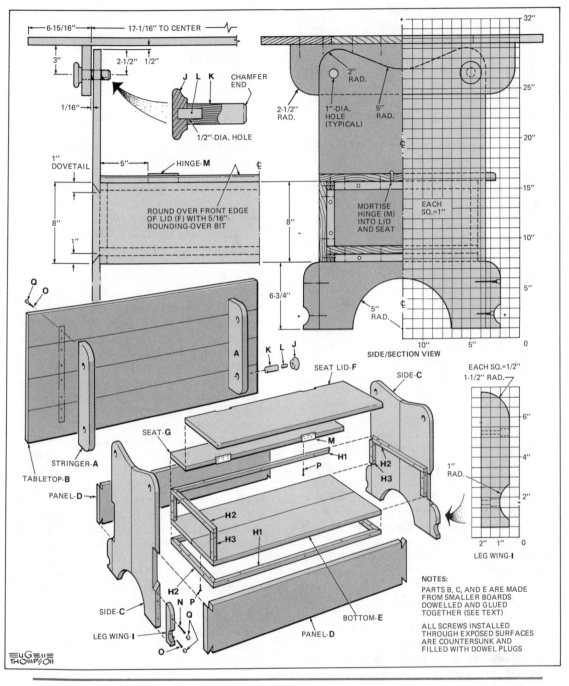

6-15/16" 17-1/16" TO CENTER

3"

2-1/2" 1/2"

1/16"

J L K CHAMFER END

1/2"-DIA. HOLE

1" DOVETAIL

5" HINGE-**M**

8"

1"

ROUND OVER FRONT EDGE OF LID (F) WITH 5/16"-ROUNDING-OVER BIT

32"

2" RAD.

2-1/2" RAD.

1"-DIA. HOLE (TYPICAL) 5" RAD.

25"

20"

15"

10"

5"

0

MORTISE HINGE (M) INTO LID AND SEAT

8"

EACH SQ.=1"

6-3/4"

5" RAD.

5" RAD.

10" 5" 0

SIDE/SECTION VIEW

Q O

A

STRINGER-**A**

TABLETOP-**B**

PANEL-**D**

SIDE-**C**

LEG WING-**I**

K L J

SEAT LID-**F**

SIDE-**C**

SEAT-**G**

M

H1

H2

H3

P

H2

H3 **H1**

H2

N P

Q

O

BOTTOM-**E**

PANEL-**D**

EACH SQ.=1/2"
1-1/2" RAD.

6"

4"

1" RAD.

2"

2" 1" 0

LEG WING-**I**

NOTES:
PARTS B, C, AND E ARE MADE FROM SMALLER BOARDS DOWELLED AND GLUED TOGETHER (SEE TEXT)

ALL SCREWS INSTALLED THROUGH EXPOSED SURFACES ARE COUNTERSUNK AND FILLED WITH DOWEL PLUGS

EUGENE THOMPSON

MATERIALS LIST—HUTCH TABLE

Key	No.	Size and description (use)
A	2	1 1/16 × 5 × 23" pine (stringer)
B	1*	3/4 × 29 × 48" pine (tabletop)
C	2	3/4 × 17 × 28" pine (side)
D	2	3/4 × 8 × 34" pine (panel)
E	1	3/4 × 15 1/2 × 32 1/2" pine (bottom)
F	1	3/4 × 10 3/4 × 32 3/8" pine (seat lid)
G	1	3/4 × 7 1/4 × 32 1/2" pine (seat)
H1	3	3/4 × 3/4 × 32 1/2" pine (cleat)
H2	4	3/4 × 3/4 × 15 1/2" pine (cleat)
H3	4	3/4 × 3/4 × 5 3/4" pine (cleat)
I	4	3/4 × 1 1/2 × 6 3/4" pine (leg wing)
J	4	1 1/2"-dia. wood door pull
K	4	1"-dia. × 3" dowel
L	4	1/2"-dia. × 1 1/4" dowel
M	2	3/4 × 3" hinge
N	4	2" No. 10 fh screw
O	20	1 1/2" No. 10 fh screw
P	51	1 1/4" No. 10 fh screw
Q	24	Dowel plugs

*Constructed from four 1×8s, each 48" long

Next, draw the 5-in.-radius arc between the two circles as shown. Because the arc's center point falls 3 in. off the board's surface, you'll need to make the simple jig shown in photo No. 3. Just nail a ¾x5x28-in. board to two ¾x¾x18-in. "legs," then simply clamp the legs in place.

Join the three arcs with tangent lines, then bore a blade entry hole and a sabre-saw pivot guide hole in the jig.

Cutting these curves with a pivot guide will assure the best cut and the least sanding later.

Also, bore a pivot guide hole in the bottom support block and cut out that arc similarly. Finish-sand all curves with a drum sander.

Front and rear panels

Cut the front and rear panels to size, then lay out the pins of the large dovetail joints on the panel ends. Cut the panel ends, then carefully trace the resulting shape onto the table side edges.

Cut the socket of all four joints and then carefully fit the panels to the sides, using fine-grit sandpaper.

Dry-assemble the four parts and clamp them in a square position. Tack-nail a temporary diagonal brace across the top edge of the front and rear panels. Now measure the exact dimension between the sides and the panels, and cut the cleats (parts H1, H2, H3) to matching sizes.

Next, bore and countersink screw clearance holes in all the cleats as shown on the drawing. Note that cleats H2 only have two holes bored in their top edges. These will be used to fasten the stationary rear portion of the seat. The front lid is movable.

Disassemble the table, then reassemble it with glue. Check for square, then reinstall the diagonal brace across the top edge of the panels and add one across the bottom edges, in the opposite direction.

When the glue is dry, remove the clamps and braces and install the upper cleat on both sides of the table and the rear panel. The front panel does not need an upper cleat.

Next, cut both portions of the seat to size and check for fit. The rear portion should abut the sides tightly; the front board should have ⅟₁₆-in. clearance on each end (⅛ in. overall). Once you're satisfied, mark the hinge positions and remove both boards.

Mortise the edges to accept the hinges, then install the hinges on both boards and carefully slide this assembly into place. If both still fit properly, unscrew the front board and set it aside. Install the back portion permanently by turning screws through the cleats into the underside of the board.

Install the vertical cleats in similar fashion, then glue up stock for the compartment bottom. When it is dry, cut it and fit it into place. Install the lower cleats around the bottom and attach.

Tabletop and stringers

Begin making the tabletop by doweling and gluing up stock to the size given in the materials list.

When the top is dry, place the poorer side down on the bench and invert the rest of the table assembly on top of the better side. Center the assembly, then place a stringer against each side with a ⅟₁₆-in. spacer between. Apply masking tape to the outside face of both stringers and to the tabletop underneath the stringers. Then mark the position of the attaching screws. (See photo No. 4.) Allow two screws per board of stock that was glued up to make the top.

Next, counterbore the clearance holes in the tabletop and the pilot holes in the stringers. Install the screws and conceal the heads with dowel plugs.

Invert the top once more, slide the table assembly between the stringers and mark the position of the hinge peg holes. To do this, slide ½-in.-thick shims between the tabletop and the top of the sides. Then insert a finishing nail into the ⅟₁₆-in.-diameter holes that were bored earlier in the table sides. Tap the nail with a hammer so it leaves an impression on the inside of the stringers. Remove the assembly and bore the hinge peg holes in the sides and the stringers.

Next, assemble the hinge pegs as shown in photo No. 6 and make sure that when installed, the top works well.

Cut the leg wings to size and shape and install them, then reinstall the movable lid and the assembly is complete.

Finish-sand the whole piece and apply the finish of your choice.

A

Above-ground swimming pool
deck construction, 2870
installation, 2875
maintenance & care, 2875
types, 2875
Air-adjustable shock absorbers,
2851
Airplanes: causing TV interference,
2900
**Alkalinity adjustments in swim-
ming pools,** 2855
AM radio antennas, 2892
Antennas
installing TV antennas, 2893
types, 2888
Artificial turf putting green, 2833
Attic storage space, 2827
Audio recording principles, 2882

B

Bandwith: TV and video, 2878,
2885
Beta video recorders, 2902
Bird kite, 2842
Box kite, 2837
Bunk beds provide storage space,
2825

C

Cabana for a swimming pool, 2859
**Capacity: determining for swim-
ming pools,** 2855
CB radio: TV interference, 2900
Chlorination: swimming pool water,
2855
Clothes island storage space, 2827
Co-channel interference in TV,
2900
Color TV
pickup, 2878
receiver, 2881
Computers
data storage on videodisc, 2884
TV interference, 2899
Contemporary pedestal table, 2916
Cupboard storage space, 2822

D

**Decks: above-ground swimming
pool,** 2870
Delta wing kite, 2838
**Diffusion filter: home video special
effects,** 2913
Digital video
Hi-fi sound recording, 2902
receivers, 2885
VCRs, 2902
videodiscs, 2883
**Diving deck for your swimming
pool,** 2866

E

Early American hutch table, 2934
Edge gluing: hutch table, 2934
8-mm video recorders, 2902
Electrical interference: TV signal, 2898

Electron beam: video scanning,
2880
**Equipment checks for swimming
pools,** 2855

F

False wall storage space, 2823
Fighters kite, 2839
Filters
home video special effects, 2913
swimming pool, 2856,2858
Flexible kite, 2839
Flying kites, tips, 2840
FM radio
antennas, 2891
TV interference, 2898
Folding snack table, 2924
French Provincial table, 2920
**Front-end service: auto (see Sus-
pension and Steering Systems)**

G

Garage wall storage space, 2820
Golf: artificial turf putting green,
2834

H

Head cleaning: VCRS, 2907
Helical recording: VCRs, 2902
High-definition TV
principles, 2880
receiving tubes, 2878
High-fidelity sound reception in
TV, 2885
Home video special effects
diffusion filters, 2913
multi-image filters, 2913
polarizing filters, 2913
starburst filters, 2913
techniques, 2913
Hutch
storage space, 2823
tables, 2934, 2939

I

Interference: TV
airplanes, 2900
causes, 2898
CB-radio, 2900
co-channel, 2900
computer-generated TVI, 2899
electrical, 2898
FM radio, 2898
weak signal, 2898

K

Kinescopes: recording TV pictures,
2878
Kites
bird kite, 2842
box kite, 2837
delta wing kite, 2838
fighter kite, 2839
flexible kite, 2839
flying tips, 2840
nikko kite, 2841
sled kite, 2837

L

Laser disc: video and audio discs,
2884
Load-carrying shock absorbers,
2851

M

MacPherson struts, 2852
Maintenance: video recorders, 2907
Movies: saving with VCR, 2911
**Multi-image filter: home video spe-
cial effects,** 2913

N

Nesting party tables, 2926
Nikko kite, 2841

P

Parsons table, 2919
Party tables, 2926
Pedestal table, 2916
Persistence of vision: related to TV,
2880
pH level checks: swimming pools,
2855
Pickup tube: video camera, 2878
Picture resolution: TV and video,
2878
Pine hutch table, 2939
**Polarizing filter: home videoi spe-
cial effects,** 2913
Poolhouse, 2862
Pools (see Swimming Pools)
Projection booth, 2824

R

Recording TV and video
helical recorders, 2883
helical recording principles, 2902
home recorder types, 2902
principles, 2882
quadraplex recorders, 2878
Resolution: TV and video, 2885
**Resort from your above-ground
swimming pool,** 2870
Restring your own tennis racket,
2843

S

Satellite antennas, 2890
**Scanning in video pickup and dis-
play,** 2878
**Shimmy elimination: auto front-
end,** 2847
Shock absorbers
air-adjustable, 2851
front-end shimmy, 2847
load-carrying, 2851
MacPherson struts, 2852
operation, 2850
replacement, 2852
testing, 2852
types, 2850
Signal-to-noise ratio: VCRs, 2902
Skimmers in swimming pools, 2856
Sled kite, 2836
Slides: saving with VCR, 2911

Sliding storage units, 2821
Snack table, 2924
Snow: TV interference, 2899
Solid pine hutch table, 2939
Stabilized water: swimming pool
    maintenance, 2856
Stacking tray tables, 2930
Stairway storage space, 2823
Starburst filter: home video special
    effects, 2913
Steering problems: auto, 2849
Storage
    attic, 2822, 2827
    bunk beds, 2825
    clothes island, 2827
    cupboard, 2822
    diving deck for swimming pool,
        2866
    false walls, 2823
    garage wall, 2820
    hutch, 2823
    projection booth, 2824
    slide-in units, 2821
    stairway, 2823
    swimming pool cabana, 2859
    swing-out shelves, 2830
    train table, 2825
    wall cabinets, 2820, 2828
Summer sports
    kites, 2836
    putting green, 2834
    tennis racket restringing, 2843
Suspension and Steering Systems
    service, 2846
    shimmy repairs, 2847
    shock absorbers, 2846, 2850
    steering problems, 2849
    vibration troubleshooting, 2846
Swimming pool improvements
    above-ground pool resort, 2870
    cabana, 2859
    diving deck, 2866
    low-cost pool, 2875
    poolhouse, 2862

Swimming pool maintenance
    alkalinity adjustments, 2855
    chlorination, 2855
    equipment checks, 2855
    filling a pool, 2854
    opening a pool, 2854
    pH level, 2855
    pool filter, 2858, 2856
    skimmers, 2856
    stabilized water, 2856
    vacuuming, 2856
Swing-out storage shelves, 2830

——————— T ———————

Tables
    contemporary pedestal table, 2916
    Early American hutch table, 2934
    French Provincial table, 2920
    hutch table, 2934, 2939
    nesting party tables, 2926
    Parsons table, 2919
    party tables, 2926
    pedestal table, 2916
    pine hutch table, 2939
    snack table, 2924
    stacking tray tables, 2930
    tray tables, 2930
Tape: selection and types of vid-
    eotape, 2909
Tennis racket restringing, 2843
Train table storage, 2825
Tray tables, 2930
TV and video
    antenna installation, 2893
    antenna selection, 2888
    bandwidth, 2878
    camera pickup tube, 2878
    color TV, 2880
    digital video, 2883
    high-definition TV, 2880, 2885
    high-fidelity sound, 2885
    home video special effects, 2913
    interference problems, 2898
    kinescopes, 2878

    recorders, 2902
    recording video, 2882
    resolution, 2878, 2885
    satellite reception, 2890
    scanning, 2878
    slides and movies, 2911
    special effect filters, 2913
    VCR tuneup, 2907
    VCRs, 2902
    videodisc, 2883
    videotape selection, 2909

——————— U ———————

UHF TV antennas, 2889, 2892

——————— V ———————

Vacation all summer in a low-cost
    pool, 2875
Vacuuming swimming pools, 2856
VHF TV antennas, 2892, 2889
VHS video recorders, 2902
Vibration troubleshooting in auto
    front-end, 2846
Video recorders
    Beta, 2902
    8-mm, 2902
    head cleaning, 2907
    helical recording principles, 2902
    slide and movie transfers, 2911
    tape selection and types, 2909
    tuneup, 2907
    types, 2902
    VHS, 2902
Videodiscs
    computer data storage, 2884
    digital video, 2883
    types, 2884

——————— W ———————

Wall cabinet storage space, 2826,
    2828
Weak TV signal causes, 2898
Wheel tramp: auto front-end, 2848

SHOP GUIDE

CUSTOMARY TO METRIC (CONVERSION) Conversion factors can be carried so far they become impractical. In cases below where an entry is exact it is followed by an asterisk (*). Where considerable rounding off has taken place, the entry is followed by a + or a − sign.

Linear Measure

inches	millimeters
1/16	1.5875*
1/8	3.2
3/16	4.8
1/4	6.35*
5/16	7.9
3/8	9.5
7/16	11.1
1/2	12.7*
9/16	14.3
5/8	15.9
11/16	17.5
3/4	19.05*
13/16	20.6
7/8	22.2
15/16	23.8
1	25.4*

inches	centimeters
1	2.54*
2	5.1
3	7.6
4	10.2
5	12.7*
6	15.2
7	17.8
8	20.3
9	22.9
10	25.4*
11	27.9
12	30.5

feet	centimeters	meters
1	30.48*	.3048*
2	61	.61
3	91	.91
4	122	1.22
5	152	1.52
6	183	1.83
7	213	2.13
8	244	2.44
9	274	2.74
10	305	3.05
50	1524*	15.24*
100	3048*	30.48*

1 yard = .9144* meters
1 rod = 5.0292* meters
1 mile = 1.6 kilometers
1 nautical mile = 1.852* kilometers

Weights

ounces	grams
1	28.3
2	56.7
3	85
4	113
5	142
6	170
7	198
8	227
9	255
10	283
11	312
12	340
13	369
14	397
15	425
16	454

Formula (exact):
ounces × 28.349 523 125* = grams

pounds	kilograms
1	.45
2	.9
3	1.4
4	1.8
5	2.3
6	2.7
7	3.2
8	3.6
9	4.1
10	4.5

1 short ton (2000 lbs) = 907 kilograms (kg)
Formula (exact):
pounds × .453 592 37* = kilograms

Fluid Measure

(Milliliters [ml] and cubic centimeters [cc] are equivalent, but it is customary to use milliliters for liquids.)

1 cu in	=	16.39 ml
1 fl oz	=	29.6 ml
1 cup	=	237 ml
1 pint	=	473 ml
1 quart	=	946 ml
	=	.946 liters
1 gallon	=	3785 ml
	=	3.785 liters

Formula (exact):
fluid ounces × 29.573 529 562 5*
= milliliters

Volume

1 cu in	=	16.39 cubic centimeters (cc)
1 cu ft	=	28 316.7 cc
1 bushel	=	35 239.1 cc
1 peck	=	8 809.8 cc

Area

1 sq in	=	6.45 sq cm
1 sq ft	=	929 sq cm
	=	.093 sq meters
1 sq yd	=	.84 sq meters
1 acre	=	4 046.9 sq meters
	=	.404 7 hectares
1 sq mile	=	2 589 988 sq meters
	=	259 hectares
	=	2.589 9 sq kilometers

Miscellaneous

1 British thermal unit (Btu) (mean) = 1 055.9 joules
1 horsepower = 745.7 watts
= .75 kilowatts
caliber (diameter of a firearm's bore in hundredths of an inch) = .254 millimeters (mm)

1 atmosphere pressure = 101 325* pascals (newtons per sq meter)
1 pound per square inch (psi) = 6 895 pascals
1 pound per square foot = 47.9 pascals
1 knot = 1.85 kilometers per hour
1 mile per hour = 1.6093 kilometers per hour

PIPE FITTINGS

 NIPPLES

 PIPE LENGTHS UP TO 22 FT.

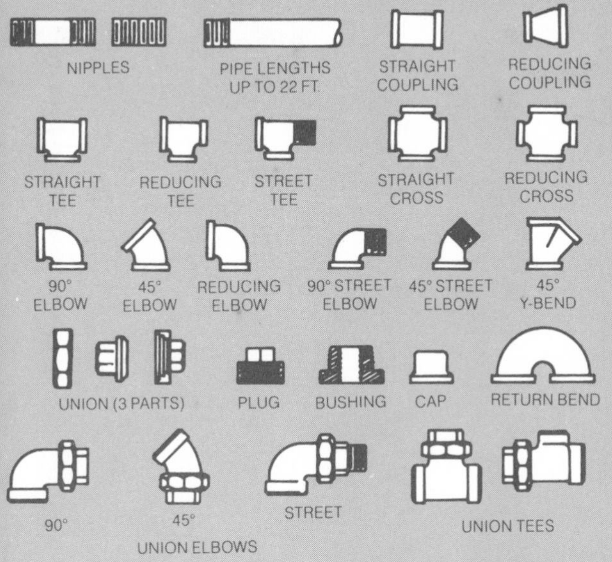

STRAIGHT COUPLING

REDUCING COUPLING

 COUPLING

 NUT

 CAP

STRAIGHT TEE

REDUCING TEE

STREET TEE

STRAIGHT CROSS

REDUCING CROSS

 90° ELBOW

 90° ELBOW

 90° ELBOW

 45° ELBOW

REDUCING ELBOW

 90° STREET ELBOW

45° STREET ELBOW

45° Y-BEND

 REDUCING TEE

 REDUCER

UNION (3 PARTS)

PLUG

BUSHING

CAP

RETURN BEND

 PLUG

 45° ELBOW

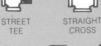 TEE

90°

45°

UNION ELBOWS

STREET

UNION TEES

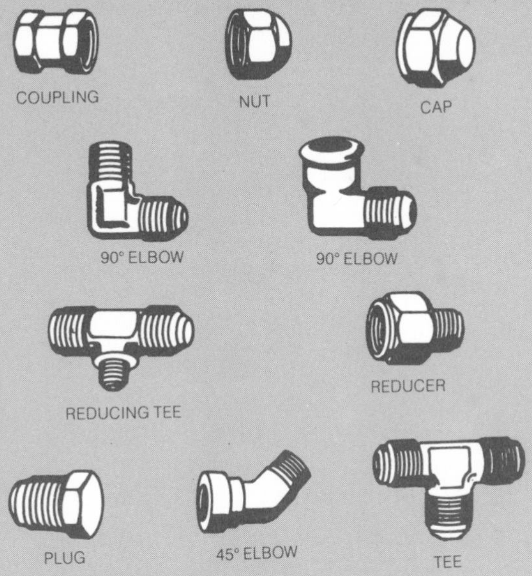

MEASURES OF CAPACITY

1 cup	=	8 fl oz
2 cups	=	1 pint
2 pints	=	1 quart
4 quarts	=	1 gallon
2 gallons	=	1 peck
4 pecks	=	1 bushel

STANDARD STEEL PIPE ((All Dimensions in inches))

Nominal Size	Outside Diameter	Inside Diameter	Nominal Size	Outside Diameter	Inside Diameter
⅛	0.405	0.269	1	1.315	1.049
¼	0.540	0.364	1¼	1.660	1.380
⅜	0.675	0.493	1½	1.900	1.610
½	0.840	0.622	2	2.375	2.067
¾	1.050	0.824	2½	2.875	2.469

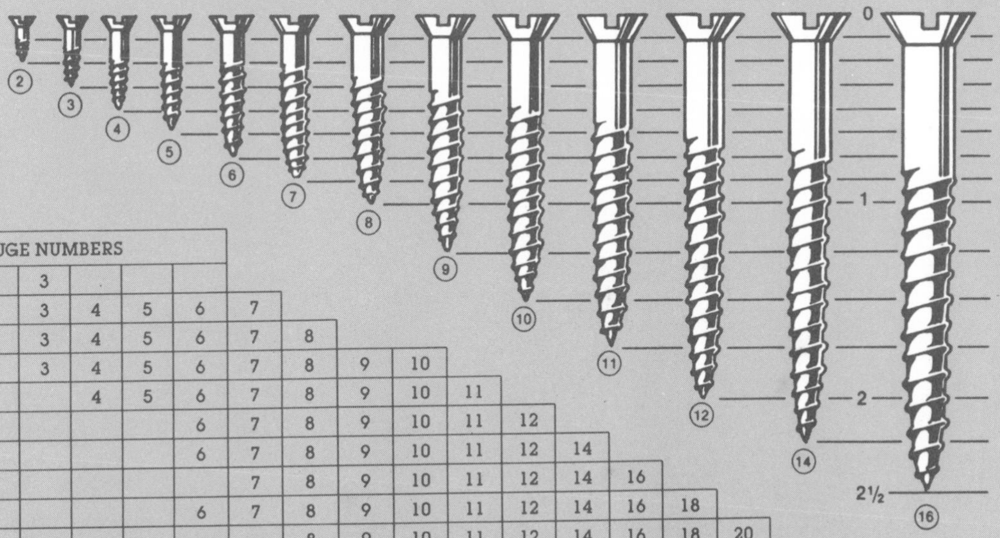

WOOD SCREWS

LENGTH	GAUGE NUMBERS												
¼ INCH	0	1	2	3									
⅜ INCH			2	3	4	5	6	7					
½ INCH			2	3	4	5	6	7	8				
⅝ INCH				3	4	5	6	7	8	9	10		
¾ INCH					4	5	6	7	8	9	10	11	
⅞ INCH							6	7	8	9	10	11	12
1 INCH							6	7	8	9	10	11	12	14
1¼ INCH								7	8	9	10	11	12	14	16
1½ INCH							6	7	8	9	10	11	12	14	16	18
1¾ INCH									8	9	10	11	12	14	16	18	20
2 INCH								8	9	10	11	12	14	16	18	20
2¼ INCH									9	10	11	12	14	16	18	20
2½ INCH												12	14	16	18	20
2¾ INCH													14	16	18	20
3 INCH														16	18	20	24
3½ INCH															18	20	24
4 INCH															18	20	24

WHEN YOU BUY SCREWS, SPECIFY (1) LENGTH, (2) GAUGE NUMBER, (3) TYPE OF HEAD—FLAT, ROUND, OR OVAL, (4) MATERIAL—STEEL, BRASS, BRONZE, ETC., (5) FINISH—BRIGHT, STEEL BLUED, CADMIUM, NICKEL, OR CHROMIUM PLATED.